Could it be your *HORMONES* love?

By

Andrea Newton

This book is intended to encourage really useful conversations and does not replace the advice of a qualified medical professional. Please consult your own GP and take medical advice appropriate for your own personal circumstances at all times.

In Her Right Mind publishing

https://InHerRightMind.com

Book Interior and E-book Design by Amit Dey |
amitdey2528@gmail.com

Paperback version: ISBN 978-1-7395590-0-7
E-book version: ISBN 978-1-7395590-1-4
Audiobook

Author's Acknowledgements

*T*here are a group of people, known as my "Tribe", to whom I will be forever grateful, and without their help and support during that very difficult phase, I wouldn't have been here to write this book or enjoy my post-menopausal years.

My son Jared is at the top of that list – our relationship is so important, and I want him to know just how much that matters to me.

My husband Kev who showed me that there are decent men out there, and my Mum and Dad who bailed me out, physically and financially, when the world was spinning out of control.

Finally, Ginette for constantly being the grown up in my business world.

To all the menopausal women out there – let's rock this!

CONTENTS

CHAPTER ONE

Why Does It All Matter?

COULD IT BE YOUR HORMONES LOVE?

*A*nd other questions *not* to ask the menopausal women in your life...

Or maybe this *is* the question we should be asking, but in a way that is helpful and not in a way that means we get our head ripped off and your claims of "but I was only trying to help" falling on deaf ears?

Who knows?

And that my friend, is half the problem. The knowing.

More often than not, women themselves don't know! According to a survey from 2021, it was found that more than 80% of women of a certain age had *no* idea or very little knowledge about the menopause, much less perimenopause. In fact 'perimenopause' was a completely new word to the vocabulary until recently.

(By the way, *peri* is the Greek word for near or around – so now you know where that came from – pub quiz point there!)

So if the majority of women don't know what's happening *and* – pauses for dramatic effect (hold on to your hat!) – more than 40% of UK Universities didn't even *teach* menopause to their medical students until recently, why the heck should you, as an innocent bystander, be expected to know?!

Well I guess if you value your marriage, partnership, relationship, friendship, job, career, peace of mind, ability to sleep at night, then you do need to know. At least the basics!

Lots of workplaces are talking about this and developing policies because there is evidence to show that:

    a. we risk losing fabulously talented women with valuable experience and expertise from the workplace,

    b. more employment tribunals are cropping up with menopause at the root,

    c. lots of men who attend the workplace sessions that I have run are also worried about their wives and partners, marriages and relationships, often hanging back to ask questions specific to their situation.

Men have told me that they have seen so many of their friends' relationships fall apart, (62% of divorces in the UK are instigated by women during their menopause years) – and are determined to keep their own safe.

There are also tragic stories out there of men who have lost their wives to suicide, with a suspicion that misdiagnosed or untreated menopause symptoms played a part.

Oh yes, men need to know about this for all sorts of reasons.

So what has brought *me* to be the author of this book and sharing these secrets with you in this way? Perhaps it will help your understanding if you know a bit more about me. Don't worry, I'll not get too caught up in tears and tantrums, well, not just yet…

For the last 24 years I have been providing coaching services, delivering training courses and public speaking at corporate events. Working with a wide range of client companies throughout Europe, I've mainly worked with managers and leaders to help them have conversations that matter.

I discovered early on in my career that sometimes things that needed to be spoken about were being ignored, avoided, swept under the carpet, for all sorts of reasons. These subjects then caused issues bigger than they ever should have, simply from not being spoken about, or addressed.

I've worked in industries as diverse as construction to television, NHS to fine wines, engineering to bread making, but they all had one thing in common. Confident Conversations were needed at every level, more frequently and consistently.

As the world has become more aware of the importance of such conversations in the workplace, they have moved on from simple disciplinary or attendance issues, to talking to team members about more sensitive topics such as mental health.

Other personal issues that might impact performance or behaviour at work have also moved into the training that I do with businesses. I qualified as a suicide intervention tutor and now menopause wellness practitioner and coach, so that I could help my clients with even the most delicate stuff.

So now you know about me in a work context – but if you are *not* a Line Manager, HR Professional, Trade Union Representative involved in this kind of workplace issue – why do *you* need to know?

Again, if you value your marriage, partnership, relationship, friendship, peace of mind, ability to sleep at night, then you do need to know!

Let me tell you a little bit about me on a personal level. This is where the shitstorm really starts to show up...

I was in my 40s, depressed, miserable, on medication and hating my life. I hated the fact that I was tired all the time and spent my life working hard to support a family. My then husband preferred to stay at home and make excuses such as having been out of the job market too long to go back after being sacked and made redundant some years previously, and he had fallen into the role of child carer.

He was still using this excuse when the child was old enough to drive *himself* to and from college, but hey! Enough of that, it brings me out in hives just thinking about it. I was feeling really rather shit and life was hard work.

I was trapped in a work cycle, a desperately unhappy marriage, juggling a big mortgage and feeling like I had died and nobody had told me. I had no energy, no motivation, completely ready to just roll over and give up. I had aching joints and several scans and exploratory surgeries and I even had to give up my heels for a while. It was all put down to "the strain of living a busy life in today's 24/7 world". I was told I needed to slow down, take time off, realise that I was older now…

With benefit of hindsight I realise that at that time in my life (which took a further scary turn), not only was I fighting a losing battle with my marriage and my business, but my body was going through its own internal battles too.

Being part of the so called "sandwich generation" of working women, juggling careers, caring for elderly parents, caring for children (especially as more women are having children at an older age these days), I was regularly hitting the wall but putting it all down to "life" as it was.

Then it happened. The shitstorm to blow all shitstorms out of the water. My (now ex) husband was arrested and then charged for allegations that make me shudder even now. With everything that was going on I was trying to climb up a slag heap wearing flip flops. One step forward, three steps back. Every time I fell, it hurt like bloody hell.

Long story short, social services got involved because of the nature of the allegations (oh yes!) so my *child* and my *family* were at risk – life became very overwhelming indeed! But what the hell has all of this got to do with you and your relationship with a menopausal woman?

Well, if I had had the slightest idea about biology, endocrinology, hormones and the like, I reckon I could have handled stuff better than I did. Knowing what I *now* know, (and hindsight is a wonderful thing), I reckon I would have coped much better. I reckon I could have put solutions and resources in place to help me, and maybe I would not have got to the point where I intended to take my own life and end it all.

Oh yes, it got that bad.

And by the way, some European research from 2009 suggests that menopausal women are as much as 7 times more likely to have suicidal thoughts, and statistically it is the age at which most female deaths by suicide are recorded in the UK (ONS). Whether it is just the hormone imbalance or the combination of lifestyle and other stressors that women are coping with in today's world we can explore a bit later on.

Now not everyone will have such an extreme experience. Granted, I was dealing with a living hell with my private life, doing my best to carry on being the consummate professional in my business life (somebody had to pay the bloody bills, especially as we now had solicitor fees too!). I had to keep my child safe from social services, social media and bullying in the village if his father's secret got out, *but* I was running on fumes and it all kept being put down to "the way life is right now".

I was dealing with this phase in my life without any support – my then husband had collapsed into a sticky hot mess and was not allowed unsupervised contact with our son, and my friends and support network were *not* allowed to know because of the shame and humiliation he felt. I was dealing with all of that solo.

Knowing what I know now, I want everyone to understand more about menopause and the impact on not just our physical health but also our *mental* health and cognitive function.

During that time my body was dealing with a rollercoaster ride of hormones – hormones that significantly impact over 300 bodily functions such as energy, clarity of thought, positive mental health and more. But they were fluctuating in the background being a woman of a certain age. Little did I know that stress and the stress hormones tend to make menopause symptoms worse (more about that chain reaction later!).

My periods had stopped (put down to stress), I was physically, mentally and emotionally exhausted and I was not sleeping, so the question of biological challenges was never explored further than "but of course, look at what's going on."

My GP tested to "see if I was anaemic/had thyroid issues/was menopausal" but all those tests came back within "normal" levels. I *now* know that the "menopause blood test" was as much use as well, my now ex-husband, but more about NICE (National Institute for Health and Care Excellence) guidelines later!

I was juggling so much stuff and eventually would burn out – but as I am sat here talking to you now, I survived.

We survived.

My son was protected from it all and only found out years later, so in a way I succeeded in my aim. My marriage finally collapsed and after a heck of a lot more crap and nonsense, I came out the other side.

Life was lighter, brighter, I was free from emotional blackmail and other such crap, I had somewhere to live again after sofa surfing for a while, work was coming in and all was getting better. I was taking better care of myself, doing fewer long distance work trips (the pressure to earn wasn't as strong as it once was) and I had stopped drinking – life was happier and healthier! And then one day BOOM! The wheels fell off.

Too many years of pedalling furiously, too long being all buttoned up and keeping on keeping on, too many masks, too much pretending, too little knowledge and understanding of what was happening to me and my body.

Hormone levels shot to pieces, adrenal glands exhausted, my stress response switch had got stuck and I fell over. Not literally, although I do remember my legs being very wobbly.

I peered over the edge, I made a plan.

My life would soon be over.

Peering over the edge had me rooting around at rock bottom for quite some time and thankfully because of the work I was doing professionally, I realised that I needed help. But no amount of anti-depressants, Valium or other such medication was touching the sides. No amount of talking therapy, counselling, CBT, EMDR, tapping my head, stroking my arms and all other manner of therapies that I was open to was making a difference...

My past had come back to taunt me. I couldn't sleep, I was bursting into tears at the drop of a hat, making my way industriously through bottles of wine and gin, just trying to find a way to cope, a chance to sleep, struggling to get out of bed, unable to pay bills and looking for a way out. Permanently.

And *that* is why I wanted to write this book.

I don't want anyone to lose their wife, mother, girlfriend, partner, teammate, colleague, sister, aunt, granny or mate into that abyss. If you are familiar with Harry Potter, it was like having Dementors sucking my life away. If you don't know about Dementors, they are soulless creatures, among the foulest beings on Earth who gradually deprive human minds of happiness and intelligence. And they were squatting in my head.

But let's be honest, not every woman will have the misfortune of being married to my ex and living through the allegations, court proceedings and everything that followed. Not every woman will be affected in the way I was. *Some* women (around 20%) won't have any symptoms at all but amongst the 80% that do might be the one that <u>you</u> care about enough to have picked up my book.

Plenty of women do write off their lack of energy and motivation and drop in confidence as "I'm just really busy right now." Plenty suggest their inability to sleep and therefore feel like crap the next day is due to "having a lot on at work at the moment." Others may think that the brain fog, lack of focus and concentration is early onset dementia; some may not even realise that failing to manage our stress levels can have a significant impact on already declining hormones. Some don't know that even if you are still having periods, you may well be on that rollercoaster ride of perimenopause (where you *can* by the way, still get pregnant. Good luck with that one.)

So *that* is why I am telling you this.

Because people need to know. Yes *people* – not just women who might want to be more aware and seek the right help, but everyone around them too.

Sometimes you cannot see what is happening to yourself – sometimes you don't want to admit it – sometimes the acknowledgement of Time's winged chariot is overwhelming and "please God, let's not give them another reason to sideline us or not hire us – so let's just keep on keeping on!"

And even if the good woman in your life *does* acknowledge it, *you* my friend need to be in a position where you can better understand, empathise and support. Especially if your marriage, partnership, relationship, friendship, job, career, peace of mind, ability to sleep at night, life matters to you...

There are lots of resources and materials out there to help you understand the biological impact of this transition; other materials to help find a solution that works, be it HRT (Hormone Replacement Therapy) or a combination of other resources. And if your someone is amongst the 80% who *are* affected, you will want to know that stuff. *But* you will also want to know how to navigate it, how to give support, how to have conversations that matter and how *not* to get taken out at the knees when you question "Could it be your hormones love?"

Some women will give up their jobs, struggling to cope; others will stop driving on motorways, at night, at all. Some women get it into their mind that their relationship, family, life, is just too, too much right now. I guess that is why at the end of my "Menopause for Men" sessions, I often have to call time, or I would be there all night with chaps asking "What can I do? I think my wife is menopausal but doesn't realise" and others who have simply said "I have seen lots of marriages fall apart at this stage — I don't want mine to be one of them". (73% of women blamed their menopausal symptoms for the failure of their relationships.)

So here I am. Getting the word out to as many of you as possible who have the sense to listen. Those of you who care enough to take the time to understand. Those of you with the intelligence to realise that *you* can make a difference.

Got it?

This is why it matters to everyone, and this is why I am choosing to bring this to your agenda. There are *lots* of resources already, but I'm not sure that much has been done to help men specifically, *and* to help men have conversations that matter about it.

Whether as a husband, partner, manager, mate or other relation – really useful conversations need to be taking place if we are to raise awareness, get help, save marriages and in some cases, potentially even save lives.

So let's get on with it shall we?

CHAPTER TWO

Why Me, Why Now?

My own life experiences took me down a very different path than the one I had previously been walking. It happened one day when I was rooting around at rock bottom and I made a desperate promise to the Universe that if I recovered, if I survived, if I made it to the other side, I would use my experience to help others. At first my intention was to simply incorporate this stuff into my Crucial Conversations work that I was doing in organisations, but I realised that wasn't enough to repay my debt to the forces that had kept me alive, so as soon as I was able, I went and trained in suicide intervention.

I have worked in that arena for several years, helping literally thousands of people to have crucial conversations, even save lives, and I am proud of the difference I have been able to make to those who needed to understand this issue in more depth.

Within that work I learned, and continue to teach, that suicide rarely happens as the result of a one-off event or issue. It's typically a complex combination of factors including identity, biology, psychology, past life and current life events. In that work I learned and teach about certain groups in our communities who are statistically seen as at greater risk of crisis. I learned about statistics showing a correlation between factors such as debt and suicidal thoughts, gambling, being a member of the trans community, victims and perpetrators of domestic abuse, people who are neurodivergent, children brought up in a formal care setting and the increased risk factor for menopausal women.

That is when the reality of my situation hit me.

It wasn't just me who felt like I was treading water, head occasionally dipping below, and never making any progress.

I wasn't the only woman living a life of fake smiles and falling into a miserable heap when the last person left the office.

I wasn't the only one prescribed anti-depressants that were not even touching the sides.

This stuff was happening to others and, given the number of suicides for women between the ages of 45-49 is a *significant* number, I needed to learn more, do more, talk to more people.

Here I am and here you are...

Now let's get really clear from the outset though – not every woman will have suicidal thoughts.

Not every woman will struggle with her mental health.

Not every woman will decide that you breathe too loudly and the way that you sneeze is cause for divorce, but if we are aware of the extremes, we can catch things before they get anywhere near that place, right? A bit like throwing someone a life vest whilst they are paddling further upstream and not letting them get to the mahoosive waterfall...

However what we do need to acknowledge is, like me, many women are not sure what is happening to them. As recently as 2021, more than 80% admitted to knowing very little or nothing at all about the menopause. Nobody tells us!

Furthermore, one of the biggest issues with the menopause is that it can only be diagnosed retrospectively. You don't suddenly wake up one day, your periods have stopped, and your body is flushing and sweating and creaking like an old barn door. Oh no, it creeps. Over time. Slowly until one day WHOOSH! You know that story about the frog sitting in the cold water and how she doesn't notice the water getting hotter until it is boiling and bubbling? Yep, that.

The menopause is only officially reached once a woman has not had a monthly period for a clear

12 months. *That* is the menopause – that date in time. So the not knowing what's happening and the uncertainty it often brings, along with a host of early symptoms, really can throw you. It causes confusion and sometimes fear and is the reason why some women actually think they are losing their minds, fear they are experiencing early onset dementia, are misdiagnosed as having a mental health disorder and given anti-depressants that do nothing to help their state. (There is currently PhD research underway to specifically look at this issue and examine the difference (if any) between clinical depression and hormonal depression. I am privileged to have been involved.)

It is only recently that I have been able to look back at my history and realise what had happened to me and when, that I was able to join the dots and truly understand. Let me use my history to spare someone else learning the hard way?

I had had those earlier experiences where life overwhelmed me and here I was again! I had no idea that experiencing poor mental health because of that decline in hormones is *not* unusual. In fact some scientific research says that menopause actually *starts* in the brain. We don't recognise it for what it is because we think menopause is *just* periods, reproduction, hot flushes and night sweats when actually, more than 80% of women will experience cognitive issues first.

In fact as many as 62% of women say the cognitive symptoms were far, far worse than any physical symptoms for them. By that we mean the brain fog, memory loss, lack of concentration, inability to focus, forgetting words that are "on the tip of my tongue, oh bloody hell, what do I mean?" and the feelings of anxiety, loss of self-confidence, panic attacks that can also follow for some of us. I've had "after the workshop conversations" with so many women who have had a strong connection with my story and come forward afterwards, often with tears and relief. One particularly senior lady was "packing up her desk" as she felt isolated and alienated in that workplace. It wasn't just my experience then.

Further research conducted in the UK in 2020, (Health & Her), found that:

* 86% admitted to suffering mental health issues,
* 80% don't even speak to their partner about this,
* 53% of the women suffered from low mood and depression,
* 50% reported anxiety,
* 42% reported anger and mood swings,
* 33% reported feelings of worthlessness,

* 77% confessed they had never experienced mental health issues prior to entering this life stage, but now did,

* 58% reported low energy and lack of motivation as the leading mental health issue, rising to 67% among 46–49 year olds,

* 9% of women experiencing perimenopause have contemplated suicide.

Let's be clear, mental health is not the opposite end of the spectrum to mental illness though. We *all* have mental health, but it fluctuates and sometimes can get stuck in the red. Our mood, our confidence, our way of dealing with the world are all clues as to the state of our mental health and for these women, they were surviving, not thriving.

Forget the bit that menopause is all about hot flushes and night sweats, trust me, there is so much more to understand. But *you* can make a difference to the women in your life, be they your partner, team member, colleague or friend and maybe, just maybe, we can make life better for everyone.

The more I was learning about this, the more I wanted to know more. I didn't feel I was doing justice to my clients, to my suicide intervention role, to repaying my debt to the Universe and so began to train in this area too. Once I started to talk openly about this subject, both on my Really Useful

Conversations podcast and in my general training sessions, I began to notice how not only male managers were showing up but also men who were perhaps concerned about their wives, partners, girlfriends, relationships.

One session that I ran for men *only* was one of the busiest, liveliest and *longest* sessions I'd had. At the end when I said "Does anyone have any questions?" an hour later men were still asking "what about", and "what if", and "what I think is..."

Men who cared about the women in their world. Equally men who cared about their marriage, relationship, partnership, job, team members, sister, mother, friend, reputation as a manager or HR or H&S professional. Lots of questions from decent blokes who just wanted to understand.

And so my idea for this book was formed. There are enough topics already that don't get the airtime they deserve. Issues that need dragging out of dark corners and putting on the table in the full limelight. People have died because of such issues. There really is no need.

We *all* need to be prepared to challenge stigma, to encourage honest, open, frank dialogue. We need to encourage authenticity and not add pressure to an already challenging existence in a world that is fast paced, future focussed and dare I say it, male biased!

Don't worry my friend, I am not going to get into feminist rants or bra burning or condemning the patriarchy (which by the way, doesn't work for men either!), but all I am going to say to you is this:

If the medical profession were aware of a situation that only affected men and it meant that your willy was going to shrivel up and become painful and excruciatingly sore, you would lose interest in things you previously had loved and had given you joy, including sex, you were not sleeping at night, you were losing your mind and your memory, your body was getting heavier, and hairier and sweatier, *and* you were having to just "get on with it, it's just one of those things" – you can bet there would be *no* shortage of HRT.

There *would* be a cure!

OK I promise, no more talk of the patriarchy – but let's just say, Mattel are in no hurry to release "Menopause Barbie" any time soon...

So let's look at the truth of the matter here. Menopause will directly affect 51% of the world's population but *indirectly* will affect 100% over time.

In my workshops and webinars, men wanted to ask me how they could help, how they could help their *wives* get help, wanted to enquire as to whether their wives' experience was 'normal', wanted to get hold of information, resources, help! Amazon book reviewers wanted more details, wanted to know how to help, wanted to better understand.

They wanted to know how to even raise the issue with their wives, partners, team members, without causing upset and embarrassment. I will never forget at the end of one workshop I delivered, one guy stayed behind. He said he wanted to ask a question, privately, if that was OK. He then told me that he felt during the webinar I had been describing his wife and he was really worried about her.

The webinar had been about mental health and the menopause – something that really bothers *me* as it was definitely my area of vulnerability during that transition. Of course I had seen the stats in my suicide intervention work, so definitely a passion project for me. Taking a few moments with this gentleman, he told me that the information I had shared had really resonated with him and he was desperately worried about his wife's mental health *and* her general safety.

He told me that his wife had recently lost her job. Poor performance was the reason. She was now at home, depressed, anxious, struggling. All through the poor performance conversations at work she had been trying to make sense of why she could no longer respond as confidently as she used to. She was desperate to work out what had happened and why she doubted her own decision-making. She could not for the life of her understand why her normally sharp, analytical mind was letting her down. She just couldn't handle the meetings, even with the support of her Union Rep – she felt hopeless, worthless and unable to cope. And eventually, she lost her job.

This can happen. In fact, this *does* happen. Perhaps more than you realise.

It is suggested (BUPA & CIPD) that as many as 1 in 4 women will consider leaving work, and 1 in 10 do. Furthermore, more than 10% will take reduced hours, decline promotion, look for other types of work that is less "demanding" – and there is evidence to prove that this does happen far too often. This can then have a further knock-on effect for confidence, self-esteem and feeling worthy, which can negatively impact mental health further. It's quite a vicious cycle if you follow it through, to the point that as many as 9% of perimenopausal women consider suicide. The stats tell us the number of deaths by suicide that are recorded (ONS), but they don't report the number of attempts and survivals, or those who experience suicide ideation. From working with literally thousands of people in this arena, all I want to say is, this stuff matters.

Thankfully it isn't something that the majority of women will experience, but there is sufficient risk that every employer needs to pay attention to, so whether you are here as a caring husband, you are the manager who conducted the performance reviews, or the senior HR manager who confirmed the dismissal – *you* will definitely benefit by being here to find out a little more.

You need to be able to support your wife, team member, employee *and* keep your business menopause friendly and safe from unnecessary grievances and tribunal claims. And, I would suggest, keep your conscience clear and your business reputation positive.

So when people ask me "*Is* there really an audience or a demand for this book?" my answer is definitely yes – especially amongst men who care about their relationships whether as husbands, partners, mates, managers, HR professionals, Health and Safety leaders, coaches, counsellors, therapists, appointed persons or mental health first aiders.

YES, THIS MATTERS TO YOU!

You're welcome.

CHAPTER THREE

The Basics

*S*o, what do you need to know?

Let's start at the very beginning and understand the basics. Before you roll your eyes and think you know all that already, let me suggest, you perhaps don't.

If, as I've already mentioned, more than 80% of women don't know, (and it is *not* all about periods and hot flushes – oh my days, not at all) there is sooooooo much more *you* need to know!

Unfortunately, until recently, the menopause was only ever referred to in hushed tones, whispered conversations, referred to as "The Change". We understood it to be a time in a woman's life where her ability to conceive and have babies ended – her periods would end and that would be a time to rejoice, no?

Well, no.

Not just that.

There is a lot more to it than that.

Let's be clear, the hormones that are all over the place during this time are *not* just sex hormones concerned with reproduction. As I mentioned earlier, they can affect over 300 bodily functions and there are 34 commonly reported symptoms to be aware of.

Forget your stereotypical narrow view of hot flushes and night sweats and the 'jokes' that go with it. Let me tell you, if you are one of the 80% of women who are affected, it ain't no laughing matter my friend...

Before we get into the 34 symptoms and over 300 bodily functions that are potentially being affected, let's understand a bit more about why this transition is such a big deal for women, as well as for those around them.

First and foremost, I think one of the biggest problems we have with menopause is the fact that it can only be diagnosed retrospectively. We don't *know* we are there until we are there.

Here's a little memory test for you – what did I say "the menopause" is?

Correct! The menopause is once a woman has had a consistent period-free 12 months – so we're never sure whether we are or we're not. It's one of those situations that we only get confirmation once it's all done, and even then we are waiting for a clear 12 months before we know it is indeed done! Confusing right?

In a nutshell, what happens is the supply of eggs that a woman is born with gradually peters out as she gets older. On average, women are born with around 2 million eggs. Unlike sperm in men, they cannot produce more and by their mid-30s the number is typically down to around 150,000.

As there are fewer eggs, there is less need for the body to produce oestrogen and progesterone – the hormones needed to look after the egg through fertilisation and pregnancy. In short, fewer eggs = fewer hormones.

Sounds straightforward, yes? However, this decline in hormones creates an imbalance throughout the whole body *not* just our reproductive organs. Every major organ from brain to heart, lungs to liver, requires a supply of these hormones to function well.

In the UK the average age for menopause (the day following a period-free 12 months) for a Caucasian woman is 51 years. For women of colour it tends to happen slightly earlier (age 49) and some research suggests with longer transition periods and more intense vasomotor and vaginal symptoms. Every woman is unique and those ages, regardless of ethnicity, are averages.

But we also know that 1 in 100 women will experience an early menopause (under the age of 40) and as many as 1 in 1,000 under the age of 30. I have even heard cases of teenagers experiencing menopause not long after starting their periods.

The reason I make this point is that age is simply an indicator, just one, and should not be seen as the only factor that determines what is happening to women. So many women are fobbed off with "you're not old enough, surely?" It happens.

But let's just back up there one moment. What we are talking about here is what might be described as a *natural* menopause.

Earlier menopause may happen for women with chromosome abnormalities – (such as in women with Turner Syndrome) and for others due to an autoimmune disease. We also need to know that some women will experience what is sometimes called a medical, or surgical, menopause.

Having a hysterectomy or ovaries removed or some kind of medical treatment (such as radiotherapy or chemotherapy) can cause an *overnight* menopause because of the removal or damage to the ovaries and subsequent immediate decline in those hormones.

These women will not experience a gradual decline or the rollercoaster that many of us do; just wham–bam overnight, no ovaries and no hormones to boot, menopause arrives.

It can also sometimes be referred to as a chemical menopause where the woman's body has no time to work out what is going on and no opportunity to adjust gradually. Sadly, there are many stories of women who have been in this position and not been given the care, advice, help or treatment that they have needed. For younger women (under the age of 40), replacing those hormones is especially important.

That wasn't something that was commonly known or understood, even by medical professionals as late as 2007. Significant research into the menopause wasn't really conducted in any depth or detail, and even today is an area that is a mystery to many medical professionals.

I have already told you that some medical degrees don't even have it on the syllabus and for others that do, it is not a mandatory topic. Thankfully that will change from 2024, but for women now, probably not soon enough. Research has fallen well short, and experienced surgeons talk about how hysterectomies were once performed as a matter of course for *any* issues with the reproductive organs, without any real consideration to the impact that the lack of hormones would have, on other parts of the body.

In the UK our health system is based on many professionals having individual areas of expertise, so often the whole body isn't considered, just the bit that there is a potential problem with.

That isn't just an issue for perimenopausal women! Even something as silly as my aching shoulder meant I kept being passed between the guy who does necks, the guy who does shoulders and the guy who does backs. To think each one might actually talk to the other and look at the *whole* person – well, that is quite a revolutionary thought!

But I digress... Back to hormones and ovaries.

There is also a condition called POI (Premature or Primary Ovarian Insufficiency) which may cause some women to experience menopausal symptoms at a much younger age. This condition will need investigating and treating as women who suffer from POI will generally benefit from hormone replacement if this happens to them at that much younger age.

Bone health and cardiac health are both at risk in younger menopausal women but with this condition those hormone levels can fluctuate like that rollercoaster that I mentioned earlier. It is possible that as many as 10% of women will still be able to conceive due to the temporary return of hormones. This might be great news if you thought your baby making days were over, but on the other hand...

When we talk about ages and stages and decline over time, we are referring to a *natural* menopause, and we need to understand that there are actually 3 stages that we need to appreciate and acknowledge.

So we know that menopause is that one day in time, right? Perhaps what we don't know is that *prior* to that one date, women will go through a stage where the most significant changes and often the *biggest* challenges happen.

We now know this time as "perimenopause" and this can typically be happening for an average of 4 years, but there is evidence suggesting for some women it can be as long as 10 –12 years prior to menopause.

This is where the hormone levels start to fluctuate and we perhaps experience early symptoms such as brain fog, memory problems, emotional swings, anxiety and certainly for me, perimenopause was a fast and scary downhill journey like a runaway train with no brakes.

We also know that other issues such as stress, alcohol consumption, cigarette smoking, weight, nutrition and exercise also affect endocrine levels and data show this can sometimes lead to an earlier menopause. Hormones alone may not be solely responsible for how we are feeling, but again a combination of factors including lifestyle and stress levels. (More about the stress factor later!)

So for a period of time that can be just a few months for some women, to as long as 12 years for others, women are experiencing perimenopausal symptoms. But because the generally-held belief is that menopause is something that happens to women in their 50's (I'm not), when their periods stop (mine haven't) and they have hot flushes (I don't) we don't always realise what is happening. We often simply just don't know enough.

So many women go undiagnosed and fail to get the help they need. It has been reported that as many as 7% of women attended GP appointments more than 10 times before receiving adequate help or advice. Of those women who did eventually receive treatment, 44% of women had waited at least one year, and 12% had waited more than 5 years.

I recently heard a very worrying interview with a lady in her 40's who was actually married to a GP, and was in ICU following a suicide attempt. She had been through these challenging circumstances with medication being offered for depression and anxiety, in fact she had even been sectioned and had undergone electroconvulsive therapy treatment (ECT). It was only thanks to her husband being Clinical Director within a Primary Care Network that he knew how the system worked, from the inside, and was able to finally help her get the help she needed, which turned out to be HRT! Thankfully, he knew who to challenge and how, but admits himself that his knowledge of perimenopause was very limited.

Please don't think simply suggesting to the women in your life that they should just go see the GP and that's everything sorted! You might need to be their advocate; you might need to encourage them to keep going back and not giving up until they are given the treatment they want or need. We will talk more about possible treatment later.

Another challenge to be aware of is that those early menopause symptoms are often misdiagnosed as depression. This can lead to anti-depressants being offered, and risks completely missing the help that women really need.

Menopausal women can suffer with memory loss, low self-esteem, disturbed sleep, poor concentration and feelings of dread, anxiety and rage. It is easy to see why literally thousands are misdiagnosed, with such psychological symptoms wrongly treated through anti-depressants or sleeping tablets.

This can lead to a cycle of huge frustration, fear and worry as those anti-depressants won't be "fixing" the underlying issue. Women then start to feel helpless and hopeless, especially if it has become increasingly difficult to get a GP appointment, or only being allowed a short set time for an appointment if they can get one, and after all that, with a GP who may not even have had menopause training.

Once more your job here is to step up, to empathise, to support and to encourage a confident conversation. I'll talk a bit later about how to approach this kind of situation and the advice you might offer to a woman in this position. Bear with me!

OK. So we know that the menopause is one day in time and we now understand that the months or years leading up to it is when the symptoms start to have impact.

We know that some women will be more affected than others – often those who have had problems with hormones before such as PMS (premenstrual syndrome), PMDD (premenstrual dysphoric disorder) or PND (postnatal depression) will be at a greater risk of debilitating symptoms now.

We also know that some women (the lucky 20%) will have very little fuss or symptoms at all – go them!

Once we start to appreciate that the hormones we associate with reproductive health (oestrogen, progesterone and testosterone) are not *just* reproductive hormones but play an integral part in so many other bodily functions, we can then start to understand why the symptoms that can occur do.

We now know that there are oestrogen receptors all over the body that need this little hormone to function consistently and well. For example, our brain has a lot of oestrogen receptors, and it doesn't just have them for decoration purposes and to make up the numbers! It has them because our brain *needs* oestrogen to function to its full potential. Low levels of testosterone can cause similar symptoms to low oestrogen, including fatigue, muscle weakness and mood changes.

Without these hormones, things can start to go awry. Hopefully you now also appreciate why the first symptoms might be at a head level rather than down below with our lady parts; that periods might still be happening; that women are still fertile during this time. Not as straightforward as you thought, right?

So we now understand better what it is, when it happens, why it happens and the difference it can make to a woman's health and wellbeing. We now understand that it is a subject that many are ignorant about, medical professionals included, and we understand some of the challenges that this transition can bring. Perhaps this is why we no longer recognise that woman that we thought we once knew!

Excellent, my work here is almost done. Well, not quite...

If you do want to know more, especially about the impact at the head level, I have found the work of Dr Lisa Mosconi fascinating. Her work is all about the female brain and she is heavily involved at looking at what function these hormones play within our brains and how the female brain ages differently. She is also making great strides on the issue of dementia, which is a condition that affects twice as many women – oooh wonder if that's anything to do with our hormones? Read her research and you will find out!

Similarly there is huge evidence indicating how these hormones are needed for our major organs, for bone, cardiac and brain health amongst others. We need to look at how we might *replace* those hormones as once they are gone, they ain't never coming back... Assuming that is the course of action wished for. I'm a big fan of "My body, my choice" so everyone needs to find their own way and not necessarily be swept along with the latest celebrity campaign. Do the homework, do the research. Women need to find the right support and advocates so they can find a way that works for them.

To the next chapter then my friend – onward and upward!

CHAPTER FOUR

Chain Reactions and Symptoms

*L*ots to learn, and unfortunately until recently, not a lot of sources to learn it from. A topic that still holds a lot of stigma and even shame, so conversations that should have been happening were not.

As a child I remember it was known as "The Change". 'She' would be "going through The Change" and it's something that was talked about in hushed tones, whispers, behind your hand conversations that kept information secret. None of that has helped today's generation of women who are experiencing it.

At school we got clear instruction on periods and pregnancy that got us through our teenage years, and when you got pregnant (hopefully after you had left school but hey, no judgement there) you were given a whole heap of information about pregnancy, birth and baby development. There was a massive library of books and magazines and information about all that pregnancy stuff – even books that gave you a day-by-day account of what to expect and how big that kidney bean was now.

After you had your baby, you might have kept in touch with other new mums – even with mums who had been on the same ward, in the same ante-natal group, at the same baby weigh-in clinic with whom you could compare notes, get advice, get sympathy.

But this menopause thing? Nope, you're on your own! After you had done your bit for pro-creation there were no more books or classes or clubs. Nobody tapped me on the shoulder in my forties and offered an insight into such things (actually with the stress and lack of sleep I was experiencing, had anyone tapped me on the shoulder I would probably have punched them in the head – in my defence I wasn't in a great place and was very fragile). That's the work I am heavily involved with today, for that reason.

I'm here to encourage society to bring that conversation out from behind the hand. To be held openly and easily – and that's why I wanted to involve you too. It's those conversations that mean we can share information, we can offer support, we can empathise, we can signpost and suggest. It's those conversations that will increase knowledge, understanding and awareness amongst the wider population. It's also those conversations that will save your relationship, marriage, job, team and ego too! I'm not a doctor, nor am I here to "sell" you a remedy or potion or pill – I'm here to encourage really useful conversations that help people get the help they need.

I am also hoping that it will also help to stop the crap jokes about the hot flushes and sweats, and stop the naff references to "power surges" or so-called banter around "needing the window open love?" Sadly as recently as today I heard an interview with a woman who worked in a large multinational bank suffering at the ignorance of the "jokers" in her team. Behave yourself you idiots!

Maybe if we all know a bit more, it will help reduce the stigma and often embarrassment that has become attached to this very natural stage in every woman's life. We can stop the loss of talent from the workplace, the breakdown in relationships and the number of women who are afraid that they are losing their mind.

Remember the results from research done in 2020 (Health & Her), suggesting that 53% of women suffered from low mood and depression, 50% reported anxiety, 42% reported anger and mood swings and 33% reported feelings of worthlessness. Tragically 9% contemplated suicide. This is *not* just about what our hormones do, this is also about how society might view us, employers might treat us, our own view of us! Over-the-hill dinosaurs who are past it with nothing more to look forward to than sensible elasticated slacks, right? WRONG.

That is why this matters.

So I am inviting you into the party – into this exclusive club where questions like "Could it be your hormones love?" may not be the right question to ask until you fully understand and appreciate what is going on, but *could* be the exact question to ask if the menopausal lady in your life is struggling to understand what is happening to her!

I want you to understand the impact and effect this transition can have for some women. It may be that your wife or partner is struggling with a GP whose knowledge, understanding and attitude about the menopause is a little behind the times. She might be the one in the workplace being "performance managed", when actually she can't help the errors that keep appearing, as her ability to focus and concentrate is shot.

It might help you because you need to have a conversation with a member of your team in the workplace, without overstepping the mark and running the risk of a grievance being slapped in. Perhaps someone has come to you to have a conversation at work that addresses a health and safety concern and your duty of care as the Health & Safety Manager means you need to address it and make reasonable adjustments as required by law. We will talk more about workplaces and their duty of care later, so hang on in there!

We've already shattered the myth that menopause is all about reproduction and sex hormones. Now let's look at the bigger picture, so that you can understand why over 300 bodily functions can be affected.

Ready? Good.

We now know that a simple definition of the menopause is "the time of life when a woman's ovaries stop producing hormones and menstrual periods stop. Natural menopause usually occurs around age 51. A woman is said to be in menopause when she hasn't had a period for 12 months in a row."

We now know that the hormones produced by the ovaries are in decline over a period of time, not just overnight, and those periods can become lighter, heavier, more challenging than ever before, rarely just stopping overnight, hence the rollercoaster reference.

So for those of you in a close relationship with a woman of this age, perhaps you have seen things starting to change gradually over a number of years? Unless of course she had a surgical or medical menopause, levels fluctuate and changes might happen gradually.

Oestrogen is the primary "female" hormone and promotes the development and health of the female reproductive organs, keeping the vagina moisturised, elastic and well-supplied with blood (it is easy to understand why we see it as directly affecting sexual function). But we often do not understand the multitude of other roles that oestrogen plays in the body, which is critical to understanding menopause at any level.

In addition to oestrogen, levels of other hormones produced by the ovaries will also fluctuate and change. These include progesterone and testosterone which again we most commonly associate with a woman's reproductive systems and libido etc. Another reason why we tend to focus on menstruation, reproduction and sexual intimacy at this stage! But a host of other systems and bodily functions are also affected by this imbalance *and* other hormones such as serotonin (mood) cortisol (stress) and cholesterol are just a few of them.

For example, that pesky stress hormone, cortisol, can make menopause worse if it starts rampaging around the body. These chain reactions where one hormone supply impacts on the effectiveness of another, is a crucial concept to get your head around.

Let's take a look at one of those chain reactions: cortisol and progesterone.

If a woman is living with a lot of stress in her life, her body is regularly firing off that stress response and cortisol is charging around her system. Progesterone is then needed to balance it out and calm the system. If progesterone is in decline naturally, but cortisol is still raging and rampaging, you can see why it can be difficult to de-stress and relax. More cortisol, less progesterone, less balance, more stress...

Progesterone is not just a sex hormone. Progesterone helps to soothe the nervous system, reduce irritability and decrease inflammation in the body. If a woman is under increased stress, (juggling a career, looking after a home, caring for elderly parents, older children, involved as a community volunteer etc.) then demand for the production of cortisol rises.

As cortisol essentially comes from the same source that produces progesterone, increased cortisol output will effectively 'steal' progesterone and cause its further decline. The body will always prioritise our response to stress (danger) over reproduction, so the source will prioritise producing cortisol rather than progesterone. Are you following this? It can blow your mind!

As a perimenopausal woman is already in a state of lower progesterone, and we know that stress reduces it even further, it becomes a vicious cycle. Not enough progesterone to calm the cortisol, so the cortisol level keeps raging, the brain isn't receiving calming signals (as the progesterone isn't sufficient to do so) and therefore the brain is still experiencing stress so demands more cortisol, which in turn exhausts the adrenals too – a secondary source of oestrogen...

Are you getting it?

Also, that stress reducing the progesterone can lead to increased levels of inflammation, which present as body aches and pains. Headaches and migraines can also be common in this situation. Did you ever wonder why stress can lead to muscle aches and pains, tension headaches and upset tummies? Cortisol stealing progesterone – who knew?! And what you now do know is that it is not all about oestrogen.

This fluctuation in hormones and the various chain reactions they can fire off can manifest in as many as 34 symptoms. I will provide a list of those symptoms at the end of this section. I'll explain why that symptom check list is important later.

Let's not forget though, this is intended to give you a better understanding and insight, not qualify you for a menopause pub quiz, so let's just concentrate on the 10 most commonly experienced and reported symptoms at this stage.

Hot flushes – can feel like flushing or tingling, and some women even experience shivering too. Women describe this as being not only very uncomfortable but embarrassing too. This isn't just "oh I feel a bit hot" – this is a mad, surging, rushing, head-to-toe feeling of burning up. So no, it isn't funny, it isn't cute to call it a power surge – for some women it is absolutely unbearable.

A Met Police Chief took part in an experiment where he wore the 'Menovest' garment (a vest with heated pads) in a meeting at work. He said he found the vest "at times uncomfortable" and "at times distracting". He said that the heat came to him in 'waves' while he attended the meeting, and as much as he tried to concentrate on the meeting, that feeling of dread as 'Oh no, here comes another one" meant that the anticipation really caused him to lose his train of thought.

Imagine wearing that every day for up to 14 years and carrying on with life "as normal"? Vasomotor symptoms (perspiration, flushing, chills, anxiety, and even heart palpitations) are the most common symptoms and are a form of temperature dysfunction. Vasomotor symptoms are also said to be the symptoms most likely to continue post-menopause too. And where is our body temperature controlled? In the brain. Not in our reproductive parts. Menopause starts in the brain! See?

Night sweats – it can be common in both perimenopause and menopause to suffer from night sweats, which in turn can disrupt sleep and our ability to get quality rest, which can impact energy levels during the day. Now you know what happens to *anyone*'s mood if their sleep is continuously being interrupted, so is it any wonder that emotions can run high, tempers can flare, and irritability is rife? *Not* our fault gentlemen, so please do bear with! In some cases, women report having to change their nightclothes and bed sheets because their symptoms are so severe. Not only does that disrupt sleep, but it is distressing, embarrassing and damn inconvenient!

And if you share your bed with a menopausal woman, perhaps your sleep is being disturbed too? So with both of you tired and short tempered, it could erupt into a difficult environment to be in. Think about the impact of this on any kids too or anyone else living in the same home!

Libido change – another symptom for which help is often sought. That rollercoaster of hormones can result in libido changes and loss of sex drive, which can sometimes cause issues with relationships where sexual intimacy is important. Now you may be aware that for men, libido can be addressed with a simple prescription for testosterone. How about if I told you that testosterone is not generally licensed for women in the UK and is not easily available. There are ways and means, but remember what I said earlier about "if it were a man?" Yup, we really need to shake things up! But back to the loss of sex drive and libido for women...

Libido changes can affect intimate relationships – for many men this can feel like a time of rejection. It can be a difficult time for both parties, but it's not that we don't love you any more – how could we possibly not?! (Unless your habit of leaving the toilet seat up, pushing rubbish down into an already overflowing bin or your buffalo-like snoring has simply got on our very last nerve, of course!)

This lack of intimacy and physical connection can cause a lot of tension in relationships and it could be for several reasons. Perhaps as result of declining hormones, but maybe also to do with poor body image, feeling exhausted, fatigued, fed up or even an issue we have not yet talked about – vaginal dryness. I mentioned earlier how oestrogen is responsible for keeping the vagina moisturised and so the decline can lead to excruciating pain and make intercourse a complete NO GO. It can become a vicious circle – tired, irritable, low libido, tension leading to bad feelings, creating more tension and anxiety, increasing stress and so it can go on and on!

(If you are reading this because of your professional role, perhaps as her boss or HR manager, you can probably skip this bit!)

But if you are in a sexual relationship with a menopausal woman, you can often feel rejected and unloved – especially if physical touch and intimacy is a sign of being loved for you. There can sometimes be misunderstanding of what is really going on, followed by accusations of affairs (my ex-husband once said to me "I think you are getting it elsewhere – you have plenty of opportunity working away". Cue enormous eye-roll at the complete lack of understanding about what I was juggling.)

Just yesterday, I heard a couple talk about how she accused *him* of having an affair because her anxiety, lack of self-esteem and self-worth had taken such a hit. Because of her menopausal symptoms she bled after intercourse, so she thought he had given her an STD from sleeping around. So much misunderstanding, confusion, blame and hurt.

It can be difficult to comprehend when men like Mick Jagger can still father children in their 70s, but sadly for women the sharper decline over a shorter period means this stage in our lives is quite a different experience. It is so important to be able to have honest conversations with your partner and realise that all is not lost! There *are* solutions to all such issues, there *is* help available, but that help is of no use to anyone if your relationship has broken down irretrievably and you are in the middle of divorce proceedings! (According to ONS figures in the UK, divorces peak for couples aged 45-49).

That's where the importance of communication and conversation comes into play and it is so *very* important. In fact we will talk specifically about the skill and confidence to have such conversations later in this book. But for now, please be aware that the ability to communicate, to manage frustrations, to engage in caring conversations matters so much more than ever at this point. To put aside your ego and your needs for now and to understand what is going on for your partner, wife or girlfriend and appreciate both the physical *and* psychological challenges of this stage? *That* will serve you so much better than hopeful jokes or snidey remarks about the lack of sex in your lives and how "you have needs too"...

Vaginal dryness may sound like a mild problem that strikes in your 60s or 70s (once the hot flushes have stopped), and perhaps cause a bit of bother in the bedroom *but* GSM (genitourinary syndrome of menopause) is a condition that affects up to 70% of women at some point, peri- or post-menopause.

Symptoms of GSM include soreness, itching and burning pain in the vagina and/or vulva, and the need to wee, desperately or more frequently. It can also mean more urinary tract infections (UTI), like cystitis. Drinking gallons of cranberry juice won't solve this one and for some women this condition can cause bleeding after intercourse – so trust me when I say there are many reasons why the desire for intimacy can be negatively affected.

If you are struggling to understand the sensation of vaginal dryness and thinking "a little bit of lube will fix it" I want you to imagine that someone is rubbing the head of your penis roughly with a cheese grater, rolling it in salt and then dipping it in acid until you get a sharp shooting pain from your penis right up to your guts and your eyes begin to water and it is so painful that you have to clench your teeth so hard that your jaw aches.

Imagine that?

Well, it is like that.

But ten times worse.

Be kind.

So yes, there are lots of reasons why intimacy and relationships can be challenging right now. When it comes to getting up close and personal, the hormonal imbalance can also cause excessive hair growth, acne and skin breakouts. It can increase body odour and if we are never quite sure when our now irregular bleeding might happen *and* we haven't had a good night's sleep in ages, you can perhaps understand why swinging from the chandelier wearing nipple tassels and fishnet stockings is *not* at the top of our Must Do Tonight or any time soon list!

For women who are affected by these symptoms, it can be a real challenge and many women will lose confidence and feel really uncomfortable with who they have become. If you are feeling that way and generally BLEURGHHHHHHH it can be really hard to muster up the energy to even make the bed, let alone get frisky in it! (There are options though, and they are not all HRT related, please do take heart.)

Now this is not the same for all women, and again, we must look at each person's situation as being unique, but if this is happening for the love of your life, please know it is *not* uncommon and she still loves you. She is *not* necessarily "getting it" somewhere else, so tutting and puffing isn't going to help you win her round, and having seen the attitude that some men, even intelligent men, have had to this transition, the divorce stats do not surprise me! For heaven's sake, behave yourself and show some empathy. Do yourself a favour, use your intelligence and pluck up the courage to have a sensitive conversation about it. (Please do *NOT* do this at midnight when you're in a huff because she is sweating like a marathon runner wearing a thermal fleece in the desert, having the window wide open and throwing the duvet off). Timing matters and the way you handle this conversation is crucial - we will stress the importance of that again later!

Anxiety – mentioned several times already - it can happen because of the hormonal levels *but* can also happen due to the other bodily changes that she might be experiencing. Anxiety can begin in perimenopause due to the drop in progesterone (which can continue into menopause too) and is often something that can happen for women for the first time in their lives. Even women who had never before experienced this, and it can therefore come as a real shock.

For others who *have* had mental health disorders such as anxiety previously, the symptoms can be even stronger and more debilitating and you might notice that your partner/wife/team member isn't as confident as they once were. Perhaps they're doubting their own decision making; they're uncomfortable in being put under pressure; maybe they're questioning themselves over and over or losing confidence in their ability to do their job, to drive at night, or on the motorway, to be assertive in a customer service situation and so on. I honestly feel from my own experience, and talking to many other women, that the menopause finds your Achilles Heel (your vulnerable places) and what you thought was long behind you, suddenly presents itself again.

Anxiety can manifest itself in a host of different ways – whether doubting oneself at work through to pacing the floor at night imaging a teenage child isn't just late home, but that all manner of unbelievably bad things have happened to them. It can be a very scary feeling and needs careful support, not simple throwaway remarks like "Don't be so soft, of course he is fine, the police would have been here otherwise!" Trust me when I say that kind of "reassurance" will not help to settle an overwhelmed, worried mind.

Weight gain – another symptom of menopause that can affect confidence and body image. Weight gain around the middle is especially common with changes in hormone levels and an increased risk of insulin resistance – another chain reaction example. Unfortunately, that visceral fat that so many women feel uncomfortable with, is actually deliberately produced by our very clever body. It realises that our ovaries are failing to produce the oestrogen we need and visceral fat is a secondary source of it!

Stress is also an issue here, as the cortisol that stress produces can also contribute to the fat. It is also a fact that as we get older, our metabolism slows anyway and we are more likely to put on weight. It can be much harder at this age to *lose* weight, so please do yourself a favour and realise the question of "Does my bum look big in this?" is even more important today than it ever was. "No love you look fabulous" is the response that you need!

Lack of motivation and self-esteem can lead to a reduction in exercise or activity, and many women will admit to comfort eating or having a few extra glasses of wine as they feel so rubbish, and then we eat our emotions too. These are not helpful strategies but when your energy is low, you feel lousy and your get up and go has got up and gone, it is really hard to lift yourself out of that dip. Eating our emotions can makes us feel better at the time but a lot worse in the longer run.

Perhaps encourage some exercise – not necessarily marathon running or mountain climbing, unless of course this was something this lady did a lot of beforehand. Suggesting a walk *together* after dinner or getting out in the fresh air at the weekend will do you both good in terms of wellbeing and is a fantastic way of topping up the mental health tank too.

Your partner may no longer feel comfortable in her skin and doesn't even like herself very much these days, which again puts unhelpful strain on her mental health. Other common menopause issues include skin problems, losing or thinning hair, once beautifully manicured nails are now brittle, wrinkles becoming more obvious, generally losing her sparkle (there we have another chain reaction with oestrogen and collagen beating each other up!) There are lots of supplements she can look at for these issues, but if she is someone who takes a great deal of pride in her appearance or perhaps has a job where she is "on show and public facing" it is important to recognise that even the most resilient of us can get upset when we find ourselves mourning the loss of who we once were (or more to the point, how we once looked).

I recently had a conversation with a stylist who works with perimenopausal women to help them rediscover their confidence, and she worked with a lot of women who often struggled with bloating at this time, which meant that at different times of the month they needed to wear different clothes and this was really upsetting for them. Please do be kind and be aware that "Have you thought of going on a diet, dear?" is not going to help matters at all! Neither for your relationship, nor for her bloating, so don't even go there. Good nutrition does matter though, so we will refer back to that later.

Memory difficulties – this one is a symptom that so many women can experience – and again as the brain has oestrogen receptors, it is no wonder our cognitive function is affected! That awfully frustrating and often embarrassing experience of "the word is on the tip of my tongue but I just can't remember it." Please don't make fun of her or get impatient when the word just won't come. Some women think they are losing their minds or experiencing early onset dementia when this happens. Knowing perfectly well what the word is (for me, the words "remote control" had been lost from my vocabulary, and resorting to "the telly flicker thing" was the best I could manage!) and being unable to recall it, does cause some concern when it starts to happen, trust me. To then feel that someone you care about doesn't care enough to appreciate the distress this is causing – that's a real smack in the mouth. (Talking of which, teeth and gums can be affected too.)

Through my work with many groups, I have heard some dreadful stories of relationships, both personal and professional, being significantly impacted by such debilitating symptoms. Women quit work because they feel as though they are not as sharp as they were and they forget information easily; relationships at home take a hit when women feel as though they are being ridiculed; they get frustrated or upset because their ability to think clearly and function as they always have is affected.

You trying to "just cheer her up" by making a joke of it and laughing *at* her just adds further insult to injury. Depending on the relationship you have, you might be able to laugh *together* at this once you are both aware of what is happening and why, but please never laugh *at* her or make her feel bad. The whole verbal memory thing is incredibly frustrating and it's certainly not a laughing matter if you feel it is affecting your performance and credibility at work too!

Trouble sleeping – apart from the night sweats which can affect sleep, simply having trouble falling asleep or staying asleep is a common feature in menopause. Lots of people refer to 3am as the menopause hour, when many menopausal women in beds all over the country are lying awake, frustrated that they can't get back to sleep and worried that they will be tired in the morning, which will add further to their concerns.

There are several reasons for this, but as with practically all such symptoms, there are things we can do to improve it and for sleep, magnesium supplements can be our best friend! However, if you are someone's manager and their time keeping and general energy at work is being affected, it can be difficult to know what to do for the best. Often a chat about temporary reasonable adjustments, maybe starting and finishing work later, might be a good solution for now?

We will talk about solutions later but my absolute top tip for anyone with sleep issues is to roll with it – develop a good routine for bedtime, log off from digital devices, be in a relaxing environment, look at magnesium supplements. I actually use a magnesium oil as I find it helps me sleep (oestrogen decline stops magnesium absorption which is needed for restful sleep and magnesium also plays a part in bone health too) and taking my HRT progesterone at bedtime also can have a helpful sedative effect.

Every woman is unique and every one of us needs to find our own way, but we know that good sleep hygiene, avoiding stimulants such as caffeine or alcohol can help and ditching digital devices a good 90 minutes before trying to sleep will help too.

Think about the temperature of the room, ventilation, choose cotton night clothes and sheets – whatever it takes to get a decent sleep. Without it, our mood, energy, patience, tolerance and joie de vivre takes a hit and our physical body is not getting a chance to rest, recalibrate and refresh. If you are her bed fellow, and you are also being disturbed (or perhaps you are the one doing the disturbing?), being tired can lead to being cranky which can lead to tension – what practical solutions can you come up with together to get the essential restorative sleep that you both need?

Talking of which – let's look at **Fatigue** – low energy is a common experience in menopause; this can be related to external stress, disturbed sleep or stress caused by symptoms. It is also worth noting that when perimenopause is happening, we are often leading very busy lives! Perhaps older children to support, elderly relatives needing care, at a stage in our career with increased responsibility and so on. It can become a vicious circle if we are not careful and in fact many women ignore their menopausal symptoms and write their stress off as being "just life, I'm always busy, I never stop" without realising what is going on hormonally and biologically. What can you do to help here?

As a partner/husband/boyfriend are there domestic chores that you can take care of? Are there caring responsibilities for either children or dependant relatives that you can find a way to share the load with others? As a manager in the workplace, fatigue is a clear health and safety issue so it will be important to risk assess the job. Perhaps discuss temporary adjustments to working hours, consider hybrid working, working from home – think about what might be a reasonable adjustment that could be made? You need to also address this issue if the lady in question does a lot of driving for example or operates machinery – please do take it seriously.

Fatigue, along with some of the other symptoms we are describing, can also be symptoms of other issues and it is important that medical advice is sought and we don't suddenly start putting everything down to hormone levels and menopause. More on that later!

And finally, one of the most common symptoms is **Irregular periods** – and irregular can mean different things to different people. They may be more frequent, less frequent, lighter, heavier, flooding or barely there until they stop completely. They might disappear for a short time and then come back with a vengeance, and it can be quite distressing especially if you a) have always had a regular cycle b) thought it was all over and it was not!

Changes in periods are a common symptom of perimenopause and normal in the lead up to menopause. For many women, this might be their first acknowledgement of what is happening, despite perhaps having experienced other symptoms already that they have not connected with the perimenopause transition. From all the research I have done, I absolutely support the statement that menopause starts in the brain and by the time our periods are affected, we are already well into that transition.

Now, having said all that, it is important to stress that not everyone will experience all these symptoms, in fact, some may not experience any at all, ever! Various research pieces tell us though that around 80% of women will be affected in some way, the majority suggesting the cognitive impact being the greatest – but I am a great believer in forewarned is forearmed. If you are *aware* that such things *might* be signalling the start of the perimenopausal years, that in itself can be reassuring for women to know that they are not losing their mind, they are not going round the bend, they do *not* have early onset dementia. Furthermore if you are also educated and there to support and empathise, *and* where necessary encourage them to be persistent in seeking medical advice, that can help.

Don't forget what I said earlier about so many women having more than 10 appointments with their GP before the peri/menopause was correctly diagnosed. Many women are misdiagnosed with common mental health disorders and wrongly prescribed anti-depressants, so if this is happening for the woman in your life, hold her hand, reassure her and help her get the help she really needs. That might mean you going to the GP with her.

However, and I need to offer a big loud BUT here...

Even though the symptoms I have described above are the more common ones experienced, they can also be symptoms of other more sinister conditions so please NEVER just write something off as 'simply' menopausal.

For example, whilst irregular and heavy bleeding is associated with this transition, that bleeding can also be a symptom of ovarian cancer.

Whilst lack of energy and motivation are definitely issues that the menopause can bring on, these can also be a sign of anaemia or other more difficult disorders.

Whilst palpitations are often reported by perimenopausal women, it is a good idea to get them checked out with a cardiologist appointment and an ECG, just to be on the safe side.

Whilst symptoms such as increased experience of headaches and migraines do often result from hormonal changes such as low oestrogen and low progesterone, they can be an indicator of other health problems too.

Stating this loud and clear here chaps — not every symptom experienced by every woman between the ages of 45-55 is menopause. There could be other stuff going on that needs to be investigated and explained.

Do be prepared to encourage your partner, wife, friend, team member or colleague to get them checked out. This is where the list of all 34 commonly associated symptoms comes in useful. Simply rocking up to a 7-minute, one symptom only GP appointment is not the best use of her or their time. They should go armed with data and make sure they are giving their doctor the complete picture. If they are experiencing cognitive issues with memory or brain fog, it makes sense to make notes and take them to the appointment. I would also strongly recommend they download a symptom tracker from my website (InHerRightMind.com) and to keep track of the frequency and intensity, and note whether there is a pattern or trend or any link to their previously "regular" monthly cycle.

(There are lots of resources mentioned at the end of the book that can also be helpful.)

It can help to take notes about triggers and lifestyle — stress, poor nutrition, excessive alcohol consumption etc. Keeping a track of symptoms, their frequency, severity, what helps/what does not and presenting data to their GP might be the difference to get the help they need, quicker and more efficiently. As I said, it is never a bad idea to track those symptoms alongside what would be their "normal" cycle – most women will be very familiar with their "normal" cycle and may be familiar with dips in mood and energy at certain times before now.

Let's sum up what we have learned here: perimenopause is the rollercoaster of hormone levels, rising and falling and gradually declining. The triad of oestrogen, progesterone and testosterone are reproductive hormones but they *also* play a part in over 300 bodily functions, from vocal chords to vaginal dryness, from aching joints to tingling skin. Recent research has produced evidence to show that these declining hormones are important to *all* our vital organs.

So what can be done about this? How can women who are negatively affected get back to a place where they are feeling upbeat, energetic and enjoying life? We will take a look at the options in the next chapter, because there are indeed options – with each unique woman needing to find her own path and combination of solutions to give her the life she wants to lead. There is no one-size-fits-all approach here. It is important that she doesn't feel pressurised into doing whatever worked for her mother/sister/ friend or favourite celebrity – remember, her body, her choice.

Finally, before you turn the page on this chapter, have a quick scan through the 34+ symptoms that we now know as peri/menopause symptoms. Not every woman will experience every symptom, and some women will experience very few. There is that unique human being again!

I've grouped them together and listed them under 4 main headings:

* **Vasomotor** – these are the most commonly experienced symptoms and include night sweats, hot flushes, chills, heart palpitations. Those hormone shifts make a body more sensitive to temperature changes and the internal temperature control can get confused.

* **Psychological:** The collection of symptoms that really caught me out and had me having a complete meltdown in Morrisons one night when I couldn't find the 'right' chicken dog chews for my hound! Also the symptoms that almost claimed my life. Not so funny in that context, right? Hormones can have a massive impact on mind and mood (if you have been in a relationship with a woman who has PMS or PMDD or PND then you will have experienced

that first hand). Symptoms include extreme mood swings, depression, panic attacks, anxiety, rage, anger and low confidence, low self-esteem.

* **Somatic (physical):** Symptoms can affect your whole body, including headaches, joint pain, sleep issues, weight gain and more. Changing hormone levels in your body can change your body's shape, size and appearance, function and sensation.

* **Urogenital (sex and pelvic floor):** Symptoms include vaginal dryness and discomfort, leading to painful sex, bleeding after sex, low or no libido, urinary incontinence and often persistent urinary tract infections.

Again this complete list is available on my website, and I will refer to the symptom tracker again when we talk later in the book about visiting a GP. Being clear in our own mind about what we are experiencing and the impact it is having, along with data, can only help with an accurate and prompt diagnosis. The NICE (National Institute for Health and Care Excellence) guidelines now in the UK are to treat the symptoms and the impact they are having, not to waste time and resource on a one-off blood test to determine hormone levels – it tells you nothing that is useful at this stage – absolutely diddly squat!

So my friend, I hope you now have a much better understanding of how those symptoms can be really debilitating for some women, and why some talk about simply opening up the front door and walking out, vowing never to return; or at least in their mind plan the purchase of a one bed apartment with a magnificent view of the coastline, that is not suitable for children, partners or pets!

The all-too-common drop in confidence and self-esteem can damage relationships, cause a woman to doubt her own ability, give up work, stop driving, decline promotion, walk away from things she has previously held dear. Trust me when I say, this is so much more than those hot flushes and night sweats that the jolly "fun jokes" suggest!

OK, I think you have earned a quick comfort break. Take a deep breath and let's come back to start considering solutions that might be helpful in our next chapter.

CHAPTER FIVE

Options and Mental Health

*S*o what options are there for women to feel better, to counteract this hormonal rollercoaster and imbalance?

How do we navigate this transition so that it isn't hellish?

You have probably heard of HRT or Hormone Replacement Therapy. Note that word please: *replacement*. HRT is not about adding anything alien and unnecessary to the body. It's not like a bodybuilder using steroids – we are simply looking to replace the hormones that are needed to live healthily and well. Hormones that the body is not producing in sufficient quantity anymore. Just as with diabetes you replace the hormone insulin, or for thyroid issues women may take thyroxine. Replacing levels. Full stop.

You may also have heard the really scary stories from 20 plus years ago where a flawed piece of research was badly reported and sensationalised in the tabloids? That exceptionally badly handled research and subsequent reporting did more to the detriment of menopausal women than it did to protect them from the increased risk of breast cancer it wrongly and inappropriately reported. An international panel of experts have since reported that "thousands of women have had a 'wasted decade' of suffering since the HRT scare" and those experts were highly critical of the way the results of the WHI (Women's Health Initiative) were presented and the media's interpretation of them. This incident may have caused a change in prescribing practice to the potential detriment of the wellbeing of thousands of women worldwide. Those experts tell us that "While HRT is certainly not appropriate for every woman, it may be for those with symptoms or other indications. In that setting, with initiation near menopause, the weight of evidence supports benefits over risks."

Outcome? We need to do our homework.

Benefits certainly outweigh risks for many women. Not only was that research flawed but scientific developments since then have brought many more varieties of HRT to the market that have minimal risk. HRT that is now identical to the body; that is absorbed through the skin (transdermal, so goes nowhere near the liver); that is made from natural product such as wild yam. All this choice instead of just the combined synthetic oral medication that was once the only option.

We need to do our homework, talk to experts, conduct our own research online. It saved my life and the only time I intend to stop using these patches will be when they're removed from my cold dead leg, unless anyone can convince me otherwise in the meantime! HRT also has the capacity to save us from later life challenges that in previous years we had just come to accept as "getting old", according to some of the more recent research, and I for one am excited to see where that goes.

More and more medical research is associating "old age conditions" such as osteoporosis, cardiovascular disease, dementia and the likes with the lack of those hormones in our bodies, so HRT is not just about the here and now, it may also be about the quality of life further on. Women are living longer and the average woman will have another 32 years in a post-menopausal body. We want to live that in a good state of health, not be in a position where we're taking copious amounts of medication for "old age conditions" (and a second medication for the side effects caused by the first lots of meds!).

Many women have been given their lives back once they are on the right type of HRT in the right dose (and as soon as possible after symptoms begin).

Admittedly it can sometimes take a bit of trial and error to get it just right, but perseverance pays.

However, there are also women who will not want to take HRT for whatever reason; or women in certain situations (often to do with medical conditions) who will not be able to use HRT as a solution, and some women may find that HRT doesn't give them the relief they crave, so please do stick with it and don't be fobbed off that "this is how it is then". It does not have to be hellish for anyone.

Please do not let an uneducated GP who has not done any learning or read any papers since that WHI debacle stop any woman in their tracks though. Encourage her to ask questions – seek first to understand – do some reading and research, read articles by credible qualified experts, listen to podcasts, get another opinion: her body, her choice. Trust me, if the symptoms really are debilitating, you have to really look at the whole risk/benefit argument and look at the many varieties of HRT available, and the other solutions that in combination could help life get back on track as before.

However, if the answer is simply no – for whatever reason – we need to respect that. It's important though for women making that choice to not roll over, curl up and live life in that state. There are lots of things that can be done to ease the symptoms, from a nutritional/lifestyle perspective: taking supplements, using alternative therapies, lotions and potions and fabulous tea – nobody needs to suffer, you just need to help her find a path that works for her. Even joining a women's network where she will meet other women experiencing the same issues can help, knowing that you are not alone, you are not the oddball. Remember the comfort of those mother and baby groups where other mums said "Oh me too!" and she felt immediately better? That.

(Unless of course she was in a group with that super competitive mum whose child did everything it should have done, and more, earlier than everyone else – that can be infuriating!)

Some women will not need to do anything differently and menopause will just be that moment in time. Others may need to find the right form of HRT and for some it will be a combination of nutrition, exercise, mindfulness, whale music and even yoni steaming if needs be (yes, it's a thing, but not for me thanks!). Whatever works – providing it's not substance abuse, addiction or illegal of course – is absolutely fine.

If the lady in your life would benefit from understanding more about such symptoms and more besides, then she would do well to pick up a copy of my *"Navigation Guide – Sailing Through the Menopause"* where we go into more detail and talk about more of the symptoms she might be experiencing. For now let's just conclude here by reminding everyone that it does *not* have to be hellish.

And you know what? Knowing that you are on side, supporting and cheerleading will make a difference too. Don't underestimate the impact if she knows you have got her back and will always be her cheerleader.

Now, an area that is a real passion project for me that I have mentioned a few times, is the impact that menopause can have on mental health. Women who have never before had issues or disorders can suddenly find themselves in the depths of despair and those of us who have perhaps had issues earlier in our lives can find ourselves right back in an almighty shitstorm.

Mental health can be affected by the internal stuff as well as the external stuff going on around us. For some women it can be a very difficult time if they realise that their childbearing years are over, and that is something that was especially important to them. Not everyone will welcome the end of their monthly periods and some may find this time challenging purely from that perspective. There are lots of potential issues at this time in our lives that could affect our mental wellbeing, and it is important that we recognise and respect this and shatter the stigma and silence that enshrouds it.

To be honest, with the more recent media coverage and awareness around mental health, more and more men hang back to ask questions specifically about this topic at the end of my seminars. I have mentioned low mood, anxiety and we have referenced the increasing risk of depression during this time. Anxiety and depression are common experiences for many women. This can be due to the lowering of oestrogen, which can also lower serotonin levels, and it can be contributed to by poor sleep, frustration with symptoms and feeling out of control. This can be further exacerbated by our reduced ability to handle stress at this stage in our lives due to the whole stress/cortisol/progesterone cycle that I spoke about earlier. I also mentioned that progesterone plays a part in our buffer and recalibration following a stress response – and clearly as that is also in short supply, our ability to bounce back from stress is not as good as it might once have been!

Stress is said to be one of the biggest causes of depression and depression can soon put a desperate person on the slippery slope to *distress* and even to contemplate ending their lives – so let's address that one here and now.

Lots of women will go to their GP feeling low, out of sorts, lacking joy, feeling miserable – so unless we are reporting the *other* symptoms and giving a more complete overview, (vasomotor symptoms for example), it is perhaps no wonder that misdiagnosis of depression is so common. We are not helping our GP to join up the dots, hence my recommendation to complete the symptom tracker and present the fullest possible picture.

There are many situations where a woman has been prescribed antidepressants which have made no difference at all to her state. In fact, some anti-depressant medications actually need a body rich in oestrogen (which a menopausal body is not!) to reach their full potency! We also know that *some* anti-depressants can make symptoms like low libido and insomnia even worse, and some have a negative impact on the very hormones that are already out of balance. Add into the mix headaches, agitation and anxiety and other such experiences, not only do they not help, they can literally have the opposite effect.

Thousands of women have had this experience and have stopped and started different types of such medication, with no improvement. They are then described as having "treatment resistant depression" and in extreme cases completely unnecessary and unhelpful treatment has then followed.

In some rare cases, families bereaved have suggested that this lack of effective treatment has contributed to women taking their own lives, and you will find several such stories without having to look too hard. Yes gentlemen, you heard me right. Sadly, there are tragic stories told by husbands of women who took their own lives, suggesting that the dots were not being joined up. Their once vibrant, happy, outgoing partners became a shell of their former selves until they got to a point where they were completely overwhelmed and made a life-ending decision. We will talk more about this specifically in a later chapter as it is a crucial conversation that needs to be had.

It is so important that we take these symptoms seriously and don't just put up with a misdiagnosis and another prescription for a different anti-depressant when clearly they are having no effect. We often can tell you ourselves that we are not "depressed" – we have spent as many as 40 years recognising our fluctuating hormones and monthly cycles. That is also why the NICE guidelines have now been changed to stress the importance of listening to the patient, asking questions, getting the full picture and treating the whole person and the symptoms that are presenting.

Every one of us is unique, but with more understanding, greater awareness, support and empathy from those that care about us, and a workplace that is educated, informed and operates a duty of care, it does not have to be hellish. Promise.

One of the reasons for me writing this was to contribute to a world where we can have conversations that matter about things that matter and not be humiliated into silently putting up with stuff. I have no issue sharing my story of suicidal intent – it's just another human condition. If it lets just one other person know that they are *not* alone, that help *is* out there, then I couldn't give a monkey's who knows about that time in my life. Please help to create a world where it's ok to talk about sensitive stuff and admit you need help?

Think about wellbeing practices and stress management strategies and do all you can to encourage investment in mental health. (Investment does not need to be financial, just simply prioritising some time specifically to relax, to put her own needs first). Life can be especially stressful at this age and stage so taking care of our mental health is especially important. Whether you are a fan of open water 5am swimming or talking therapy with a trained counsellor, we need to encourage the women in our lives to do what works for them!

In many communities around the world older women are seen as leaders with considerable power and status. Wisdom having moved from the womb, with the ability to create life, to the heart and becoming an elder in many countries means being elevated to a place of honour. That's quite different to the attitude of "Crack on as normal Sharon, and what's for tea tonight?"

In fact, a professor at Yale Medical School noted that "in societies where age is more revered, and the older woman is seen as the wiser and better one, menopausal symptoms are often significantly less bothersome." It's an interesting one to consider that the attitude of the people around us and the Society within which we live can make a difference to how well we navigate this transition.

So why not take a breather now yourself. Reflect on the difference that attitude and expectations can make and review the essential learning from this chapter whilst you make tea?

CHAPTER SIX

Menopause Conversations – the GP

*T*here is still such a stigma around the menopause. Conversations are still happening behind hands or in hushed tones and it doesn't have to be that way. The more we can help women in our lives to find what works for them so that they can then choose to see this as a fantastic opportunity, the better. On average women will be living for another 32 years after reaching menopause, so it makes good sense that we invest in our wellbeing to make the most of that time.

Don't forget the notion of the "Second Spring" that Chinese medicine refers to, and the fact that women of that certain age are full of wisdom, knowledge and expertise. Life without periods and the risk of an unwanted pregnancy can leave many women feeling liberated and energised. Many will enjoy the years when any children are finally moving on with their own lives and they are no longer providing a taxi service, cooking four different meals to accommodate everyone's hours and having to deal with "he said/she said" squabbles.

Many women of that certain age will invest in their own wellbeing now because they finally have the time, opportunity, and budget to do so. Self-care does not have to include candles and sandals and yoga and massage if that is not their thing though! Encourage variety and support women to choose the path that works best for them. Around the world other cultures celebrate that now really is the time for women to put themselves first, and that is not a bad lesson to take on board if life feels overwhelming right now.

Practicing gratitude, celebrating the positives, journaling, enjoying fresh air and time in nature, choosing to nourish mind and body, and if so inclined, get involved in open water cold swimming, which seems to be all the rage just now! (Personally, my preference will be for a hot bath at the other end of the day with a chance to unwind and detox from digital devices before bed, but again each to their own!) Life does not have to be horrendous and simply tolerated, and the more we find the route that works for each one of us, the healthier, happier, and more enjoyable our relationships with YOU will be!

We must consider the impact that menopause and that transition can have for the relationships in our lives – whether at home, at work, with our social circle, with members of our family or community. For the 20% of women who sail through, there may be no change at all but for others, that transition can be full of tension, frustration, irritation and damaged relationships.

It could be a marriage upset by the lack of libido, sexual intimacy and fun, or a friendship strained by a lack of motivation to engage and understand, (common amongst friends who might have quite different menopause experiences). Relationships in the workplace might also change, especially with one's line manager if performance, attendance or results are affected during this transition, again dependant on the severity of symptoms and the nature of the role. Let's take a look at relationships with people around us now. You might find it strange that I want to talk about the relationship with the GP or medical professionals first!

Think about it though: if my levels are running lower than I need them to be then my ability to engage with you in a loving, productive, carefree manner is going to be somewhat challenged. Let's get my physical levels sorted, with appropriate advice, treatment, or support in place first and go from there.

As I suggested earlier, before you picked up this book, you might have thought it was as simple as go see the GP, get sorted, job's a good one, right? As a manager you might have been suspicious that that team member was being a malingerer, telling you they had had GP appointments but were not feeling any better for it. But now that you know that some GP's have never been menopause trained, which means many will be uneducated and stuck with the memory of the flawed WHI research that was all over the press at the time!

Thankfully this is being addressed more consistently these days and many more medical professionals have taken on training, but we still do not have a perfectly joined up system. 2024 will be the year where it appears on more of the syllabus, so hurrah for that at least!

Although more GP's are now learning and understanding about the menopause, only a very small percentage would be considered experts in this field. It may be the case that if a woman is struggling with her symptoms (and is lucky enough to be able to afford it) she will seek a private consultation with a trained menopause expert in order to get the up to date, specific and relevant advice for her personal circumstances.

Be aware that such options are out there. With the internet the whole country and range of services is only a mouse-click away and in certain cases getting out your credit card, where feasible to do so, can get you to a satisfactory outcome much quicker. That was the route that I had to take as I was peering over the edge and rooting about at rock bottom and my GP had suggested they "take me off all my meds for a while and start again". A friend was so worried about that advice that one weekend she arrived on my doorstep and told me she was staying with me for the next few days, such was her concern for my wellbeing at that time. The £135 I spent the following Monday was probably the best money I have ever spent on myself! (Although I have shoes that come a close second!)

Now don't get me wrong, there might be a wonderful, proactive GP at your local practice who has made it their business to find out as much as possible. A GP able to guide and advise and prescribe perfectly, following the latest NICE guidelines and treating the symptoms that are being presented. Just please don't be surprised if this is not the case for everyone, everywhere.

Some recent research revealed that 39% of women interviewed did not trust their GP to diagnose the perimenopause and a significant number of women (36%) said they had to visit their GP three times or more before a correct diagnosis was made.

Evidence also suggested GPs were poorly informed and sometimes unsupportive with many women wrongly diverted to mental health services or misdiagnosed with anxiety or depression. Some GPs have also got a bit blasé about it recently calling it "the Davina effect" – believing that women now just wanted HRT because of a Channel 4 documentary, and some were a little patronising in that regard.

It was suggested that such difficulties were often even worse for LGBT people, younger women who did not fit the "menopause age bracket" and women of colour. It is important to be realistic in terms of what to expect from the local GP and so I am going to offer some advice for you to share so that the women in your life feel better prepared and able to both make the best of this appointment and make sure they are heard and understood. It's also far easier for the GP if they can see that this person has done some research, is clear in her own mind about the symptoms she is experiencing, and can talk directly about the key issues she is dealing with.

I never thought that the decades I have spent in organisations training people to have confident conversations in an assertive way would come in handy in my later years as menopause advice but I have to say, it really does make a difference.

First, as already suggested, I would encourage any woman to download a symptom tracker from my website (InHerRightMind.com) or one of the many online resources available today such as on the Newson Health balance-menopause.com, or menopausesupport.co.uk or another good site is rockmymenopause.com. On those websites and many others that I will list in the resource section for you at the back of this book, the free to download symptom checker is a great place to start, along with information about symptoms that can all help in your preparation for a visit to the GP.

Track symptoms for a couple of weeks, noting frequency, intensity, duration etc. so that before the GP visit, there is a chance to build up a clear picture of what she is experiencing over a reasonable period of time. Keeping the tracker will help her be objective and offer specific examples to help the conversation she is going to have with her GP. Take into account the "normal" menstrual cycle that she was used to and see if there is any direct relationship. Are symptoms better/worse at different times of the month? If so, when?

When it comes to the time to make an appointment with a GP, it is worth asking if anyone at the surgery is a menopause expert or has it as a special area of interest. If so, insisting on making the appointment with them is a good move. Keep in mind, her body – her choice.

Before going, I would also take a moment and ask her to have a think about what she would like to achieve from the appointment. What would she like to have happen? That might be that she wants further investigation into some symptoms, it may be that she would like to be more informed about HRT options that might be suitable or she may want to find out about any local groups or networks of menopausal women in that local area/health authority. Thinking in advance about what she might want to gain from it will be useful and stop that moment of panic when faced with "the expert" where we thank them for their time and then kick ourselves all the way home because we forgot to say, or we didn't ask, or we felt we couldn't...

Is she simply looking for confirmation that her symptoms are peri/menopausal or is she hoping for a prescription for HRT, for example? Start with the end in mind but don't be disappointed if the GP wants to check bloods or blood pressure or any other investigative procedures before prescribing. As we said before, many menopausal symptoms can also be symptoms of other issues or more serious conditions, so let's also get them ruled out! Remember though that because hormone levels fluctuate, a blood test purely to test for whether a woman is perimenopausal is *not* effective or correct treatment (and is not the current NICE guidelines approach either! You might even go to the NICE website and download the most current guidelines so that you can reassure yourself what your GP should be doing – these guidelines have recently been updated and are due again in November 2023).

She might go as far as to do her own research regarding HRT and what she feels would be best for her, if that is a route she wants to consider. There are some really helpful online communities on social media that are worth visiting, and lots of helpful information on websites that can be informative and educational. The better informed and aware she is, the more confident the conversation with the GP, the more likely she is to come away at least feeling satisfied that she has said what she wanted to say and has been heard. GPs are trained to know a little about a lot, so it is unfair of us to expect them to be experts in all areas. However, given 51% of the population will experience menopause, I'd be a strong advocate for them knowing a wee bit more, for sure!

Once in front of the GP, she should start by stating factual examples of what she has noticed. Invite the medical professional or GP to comment with their thoughts. She should ask for what she would like to now happen. Agree a way forward *with a review*, just in case!

It may be that her GP is totally switched on and familiar with the current guidelines that they should be following, which are very much in favour of "treating the symptoms as presented, with the patient describing the effect they are having", but if not, encourage her to remain calm, assertive and clear about her research and the outcome she would now like to consider.

If the GP has a different opinion, she should hear them out and ask them why they feel that is the most appropriate course of action. If she agrees with them, make arrangements for any blood tests or investigations as soon as possible and explain that if there are no concerns about other issues or underlying symptoms, what she would like to have happen next.

The final piece of advice I would offer at this stage is that this is an appointment that you (or another supportive person) might go along to as well if she feels she would benefit from it. Clearly that depends on your relationship, and I am thinking more about husbands/partners/family members/ friends here rather than you as a manager with a member of your team, obviously! But if she feels that by getting her partner/spouse/friend to accompany her in case she needs that emotional boost to get the treatment that she wants, then support that. Of course it might not be necessary, she might feel perfectly capable of dealing with it on her own, but perhaps just let her know (especially if she is feeling completely out of sorts) that you will go along if she would like that, even if just to wait outside in the car. Offering moral support can be very much appreciated. Please *do not* tell her you *will* be attending or make her feel as though she is not capable of speaking for herself – she is possibly perimenopausal not incompetent.

I well remember my own experience where my GP wanted to "stop all meds" and leave me for a few weeks. I was simply too overwhelmed to object and luckily my good friend stepped in and pointed out that leaving me with nothing at all probably wasn't the best thing given my state and my history – phew! Consider each person and their situation but let them know you care and that you are there, physically or metaphorically to provide whatever level of support they would like. A great investment in your relationship if handled well.

Don't be offended if they want to handle it solo though – again, each to their own and whilst I am grateful for the support I had at the time (going to the post office to buy a stamp was overwhelming), if anyone decided to come along with me now, I wouldn't be so welcoming!

Encourage and support, don't take over and patronise? That's the way to do it, she said, in a non-patronising way...

CHAPTER SEVEN

Menopause Conversations – at Home

*B*ut what about at home? What about *your* conversation and the support that *you* want to offer?

"Could it be your hormones, love?" which is where we started with this book could indeed be the best question anyone has ever asked – especially if she has no idea herself what is going on but is concerned about the changes she has noticed and the way she is feeling. You don't need me to tell you though that the timing, tone of voice, current context is important though, right?

I would always, always, *always* suggest that you give any conversation of this nature the benefit of preparation so that you can do your best to say what you want to say, how you want to say it and it be received in the way that you intended. Let's be honest, you can control what you say, you cannot control how she hears it and replies though, so we need to put some work in.

First of all I would find yourself a quiet moment away from "stuff" and make a few notes. Have a think about perhaps things you have noticed that are giving you cause for concern or think about things she has said to you which *she* is concerned/bothered/worried or even pissed off about. (That's a technical term and can only be used in specific circumstances, by the way!)

So a good place to start are some specific, factual examples that we can describe objectively, without any sarcasm or judgement.

Make a note of a couple of specifics, don't be going into this conversation with some vague, waffly, all over the place ramble that is going to create misunderstanding and upset. Bear in mind what you have learned about the impact that perimenopause can have, how sensitive she might be feeling about herself and her experiences, and tread with care!

"Shall I make us a cup of tea? I thought we could just grab a few minutes whilst everyone else is out to talk about what you said last night about feeling like you'd been hit by a bus and just had no motivation to do anything."

Use the language she has used if you can, do not paraphrase or translate it into your own words, try as much as possible to specifically use the words you heard her use. Two benefits: she now knows you were listening and by using her words you are less likely to either trivialise or exaggerate from your perspective.

"When you said that, I could tell that you were feeling pretty upset, and I am worried about you."

Let her know *why* you want to have this conversation. Give specific issues that are worthy of discussion and explain *why* you are now bringing it up. She does *not* need to feel told off, judged or criticised – she needs to feel understood.

"I know you said you have been feeling like that for a while now, and I also noticed that you didn't want to go to your craft class this weekend, and that's not like you. Shall I put the kettle on?"

Once you have specifically expressed your concern and let her know that it is concern, not any other motive or intention, the next step is to *invite* conversation.

Now let's be *really* clear about this: communication and conversation are TWO DIFFERENT THINGS.

I'll say that again for clarity.

Communication and conversation are two different things and *here* we want to engage in supportive, meaningful and worthwhile *conversation* which means it is a two-way street. It means you must use questions and listening skills as well as sharing information.

Questions that are open and invite her to talk to you more:

"Talk to me about what's been going on? Any thoughts on what it is that's making you feel this way?"

Questions like:

"How long have you been feeling like this? Did you notice when it first started?"

Not because you are going to diagnose, advise or suggest a solution; (please step away from any solution) but to focus on understanding how she is feeling, what she is experiencing and gather information. You are inviting more information so that a) you can start to understand the full picture and also b) so she gets to say it out loud to someone who cares. Trust me when I tell you that you should never underestimate the power of simply listening, but listening to understand, not just listening to reply!

Questions such as:

"Have you spoken to anyone else/anyone at work/any of your friends about it?"

Try to gauge how much this has been on her mind, and what advice she might have already had. Get a feel for how big a deal she thinks this is.

Depending on the response you get, which can range from "I don't want to talk about this right now" to "Actually there's a whole load of stuff that has been bugging me, if I am honest – how long have you got?", you can decide on your next step.

If she doesn't want to talk about it right now, that's absolutely fine – let her know that's OK and let her know that when she is ready, you would be happy to listen and to help in any way you can. If she is upset and says she cannot talk to *you* about it, perhaps ask if there is anyone that she feels she would benefit from talking to – but I would hope that if you have a strong relationship you can talk about practically anything. If not, there is work you could do!

Again, if you are thinking about this conversation in the context of a friend or someone at work then you may not be the person they want to confide in, and that is OK – is there anyone you can signpost them to that they *would* benefit from, especially if this is a workplace issue?

Whatever she chooses to share with you, listen, pay attention, acknowledge. Do *not* trivialise it, tell her it will blow over, suggest she gives herself a good shake or sweep it under the rug with a "well you have been really busy recently so no wonder you feel that way. All you need is a good night's sleep." *That*, my friend, is the sort of answer that would leave you in no doubt of my feelings, I promise!

Describe what you have noticed.

Explain why you are asking.

Invite her to tell you more.

Listen, listen and listen some more.

Only once you have done all of this and feel that you have understood (listening to understand, remember) then think about action – what does she want to do about this? If anything? And again, that is *her* choice. You might be worried about her, she might just want to sit with it for a while longer and this first conversation might only be about helping her talk about it out loud and know that you are there and on her side. Chief Cheerleader but no pom poms required, thanks.

So the framework that I am encouraging starts with prep – getting clear in your own mind what you want to say, how you want to say it, specific examples *and* the timing of the conversation. One thing to be aware of is that sometimes conversations happen more easily when you are side by side rather than face to face, so you remember that "walk after dinner" that I suggested earlier? Sometimes people find it easier to talk alongside rather than across from, but you know best what will work for you, I'm sure.

Then we describe, explain, invite, listen and agree the next step and if I was that way inclined I would have been able to make that into a fancy acronym and sold it for a fortune, but I am not here to impress you with my acronymising – and yes, I know there is no such word but...

To summarise:

Describe – factually, objectively, no judgement, no criticism

Explain – I'm asking because I am worried/concerned/ it's out of character for you...

Invite – tell me, talk to me, help me understand

Listen – it takes energy, focus and effort but is essential to meaningful conversation and trust me when I say, listening can change and even save lives!

Agree action – and that action might be "Let's talk about this again when you have had chance to think about what you would like to do."

It doesn't hurt to end a conversation like this with a hug or physical touch, again depending on your relationship (please don't do either of those things if you are her manager or that will just land you in bother. Don't say I didn't warn you!). It's just a way of saying "I care", which in our house would be to carry on with that cup of tea and magic up a donut too. Just saying!

I still remember the conversation I attempted to have with my *now* husband back in the early days, when

I was weeping and wailing and wobbling around (global pandemics don't much help) and seeing as he was the one that was most affected by my behaviour (during lockdown – oh joy!) it just had to be done.

Now he is a lovely man, very Northern, very down to earth, very lacking in knowledge about the menopause and not terribly good at the more delicate stuff, but thankfully he wanted to understand and do all he could to support me.

He did an awful lot of "it'll be ok" as his best offer, which although not inspiring was at least reassuring, but I have heard other stories where partners can struggle with what is going on, especially if there is tension in the relationship due to mood swings and sudden changes, and tension in the bedroom doesn't help either! Please *do not* attempt to have a meaningful conversation at 3am when you are both tetchy, tired and totally pissed off (there's that term again) with the whole interrupted sleep thing though!

On a serious note I'm aware of many couples whose relationships have taken a real hit during this time. There have been coaching clients who have talked about their difficult conversations with partners and wanting to just open the front door and walk away into the night. Women who have felt so uncared for and unloved – generally just because he was uncomfortable in expressing concern and talking about such things. Even couples who divorced and then got back together again when she was on HRT! As always, some who have just sailed through it like a Sunday morning stroll in the park too – good on them!

Sometimes one of the hurdles is if their partner has a view or has heard about someone else's experience where they have "sailed through the menopause without any issue", so why can't you? My honest belief is that anyone who has "sailed" and *nothing* has been affected by their transition, is either fibbing or bloody lucky!

Please do remember that we are *all* unique and we will *all* have quite different experiences. Your only concern should be the experience of *your* partner/wife/girlfriend and not comparing to someone else who has been out hugging trees and listening to whale music rather than sinking the gin that your partner is hell-bent on having!

I mentioned earlier some of the tensions and frustration around intimacy – whether women who would rather stab out their own eyes with a rusty spoon than engage in intimate behaviours, or partners who feel unloved and rejected. I have to say, this is another part of the relationship that will benefit from a really useful conversation.

Right time, right place, right preparation but please don't tell me that you can't have such a conversation with the one person who you have been "up close and personal with"? (I'll not use the exact phrase that a coaching client once used, but what she suggested was "if you have had oral sex with this person but you can't talk to him about your menopause then..." – it loses a little with the language cleaned up, but I'm sure you get my drift!)

One of the challenges we have in this arena is that there is often a real misconception about what the menopause actually is and how wide and varied the list of symptoms can be. Now that you have had the benefit of this book, and a chance to learn more, you really do need to get comfortable with the uncomfortable and have a conversation that matters. You could even tell her that you have read this book as you were concerned and wanted to understand what was going on for her so that you could be supportive – that may well get you Brownie points for being a pro-active caring partner! If *she* bought you this book, how flipping insightful of her – it's time to talk my friend!

CHAPTER EIGHT

Menopause Conversations
– With friends or with the boss

*A*nother relationship that might be unusually affected at this time might be the relationship she has with friends and other females. If they are at the same stage and having very different experiences, it can be a strain on the relationship if the one who is "doing better" isn't emotionally intelligent enough to realise that, but it can also be tough if she has friends who are perhaps younger or who she works with, that have no notion about this and might be a bit "get a grip lady!" Whilst it can be good to have people around you who are experiencing similar issues, comparison is often the thief of joy and even of friendships!

There can also be strong feelings about HRT or not HRT, especially if one thinks it is the work of the devil and that you must "put up and power on regardless" and the other is happily slapping a patch on and skipping through the daisies. On the one hand, girlfriends can be a whole heap of fabulous support as she embarks on this journey into Second Spring together but I have seen some friendships deteriorate where it has become something of a competition as to who was having the worst time!

Some people will hold some quite strong beliefs about what women "should" and should not be doing. Some will do their best to persuade her that their 5am cold water open swimming experiences along with a special brew of nettle tea is the *only* way to go! My advice to anyone in that situation is to always find your own way and if she can, to find a supportive friend or group or forum where her experience is respected and supported. There are some excellent online groups these days where women are having intelligent, educated, and supportive conversations so that might be a good place to signpost her if necessary? Sometimes we just need to know that we are not alone, we are not odd or pathetic or "giving up too easily". Think back to other such differences between women such as breast-feeding v bottle, cry it out or cuddle, wax or pluck, jam or cream on your scone first, you know, that kind of thing! Reassure her that she needs to do what is right for her (as long as it is not unhealthy and risks causing harm as noted earlier) and that you will support her in that.

There are now also folks like me, trained specifically as menopause coaches, who can offer that additional support and action planning, should it be needed. We can do it from a quite neutral, experienced, informed place and help someone think through any such challenging situations with the emotion removed. Of course when I left school I told the careers officer that one day I would be a menopause coach... (Yeah right.) But seriously, for any woman who wants to have the time to unpick that big fat mound of spaghetti-like strands that are all mixed up and get clarity, it can be a damn sight cheaper to work with a menopause coach than a divorce solicitor! It could be time well spent that helps her to get non-emotive, non-judgemental support and find a way to continue a successful career and not write herself off.

Now talking of the workplace, that can be a whole arena of trouble and angst, depending on where she works and the culture of the business. It will also depend very much on whether the organisation has done any work around menopause awareness (many have) and whether Line Managers, HR and H&S professionals have been trained (some better than others!) as to the experience she may well have there. If you *are* a manager or work colleague then this next bit is going to be especially important for you, so let's dig in!

As a peri/menopausal woman in the workplace, with a job to do and results to achieve, there may be days when she finds that she is just "not herself". According to research, two thirds of women working through the menopause say they currently have no support at all from their employers; 25% of women say they have considered leaving their job; according to reports on CIPD (Chartered Institute of Personnel and Development) website, 1 in 10 actually do end up handing in their notice. Other women have reduced hours, gone part-time, stepped down in authority to reduce responsibility or refused any further development, promotion, or progression. What a tragic waste of experience, expertise, talent, and wisdom and definitely time with a trained menopause coach can be helpful here before any life-changing decisions are made.

I was only recently listening to a piece on the radio about employers counter-offering to keep employees and not lose them to competitors, but we should not just be concerned about losing to the competition, we need to think about retaining that talent, full stop!

Decent employers should be paying attention to this and doing all they can create and maintain a menopause friendly workplace. In the UK alone, that represents about 1.3 million women, and losing any of this experience from the workplace due to poor employment practices and untrained managers is costly and unnecessary. Legally too, they have a duty of care to protect all employees' health and wellbeing at work. If reasonable adjustments are required, they should be made wherever possible, as with any other medical condition or disability. We will be coming back to that word later.

Legally, employers have a duty under both the Health and Safety at Work Act and also under the Equality Act 2010, where a person should not be treated any less favourably and where there are nine protected characteristics. Age, gender and disability are three of them – keep those in mind for later too!

Financially, organisations will also be wanting to do the right thing by their staff. Three out of five (59%) working women between the ages of 45 and 55 who are experiencing menopause symptoms, say it has a negative impact on them at work. (This is according to research from the CIPD, the professional body for HR and people development.) Furthermore, this has led to almost a third of women surveyed (30%) stating they had taken sick leave because of their symptoms, but only a quarter of them felt able to tell their manager the real reason for their absence.

Privacy (45%) was the number one consideration for women choosing not to disclose. A third (34%) said embarrassment prevented them from saying why they had to take time off and another 32% said an unsupportive manager was the reason.

If organisations are not doing the right thing, they are going to be affected financially by the cost of sickness absence, unable to record or monitor the real costs, patterns, or trends, as women are uncomfortable disclosing. Financially any sickness or absence can lead to a dip in performance, stress on other team members, dissatisfied customers, deadlines being missed and in certain job roles where minimum staff numbers are required to operate legally (e.g. fire service crews), it can cost a heck of a lot more.

The menopause reportedly costs UK businesses *14 million working days each year*, the equivalent of £1.88 billion in lost productivity and that's before we get into women who leave work one day and don't ever come back!

We talked earlier about women leaving the workplace, dropping down to part time hours, refusing any promotion or progression and so on – what is the cost of that talent, expertise and experience to any business?

Research shows that 50-year-old women who reported one problematic menopausal symptom at the age of 50 were 43% more likely to have left their jobs by the age of 55 and 23% more likely to have reduced their hours (Women and Equalities Committee: Menopause and the workplace, 2021 House of Commons). The same meeting went on to discuss how the cost of replacing an employee in the UK can reach upwards of £30,000 (re-training and recruitment costs). That's a hefty cost to any business, especially in the current economic challenges and war for talent in the UK! Plus, given that many menopausal women are often at the peak of their careers at this age, how do you put a value on that?

Consider that the ONS (Office for National Statistics) data tell us that "menopausal women are the fastest growing workforce demographic" so that is an awful lot of expensive talent, expertise and experience that we risk losing or missing out on. Our ability to attract new talent will be further impacted should the organisation damage their reputation due to their lack of support of these employees, or worse still, the outcome of a tribunal with media in attendance. Everyone has got a lot fussier about where they choose to work since the pandemic and a reputation should be protected at all times if an employer wants to reasonably be considered an employer of choice.

And talking of those tribunals, they can hit hard on the bottom-line profitability of the business and not just its reputation locally. The number of tribunals with menopause symptoms at the root of them has steadily increased in recent times. Do you remember earlier I pointed out those protected characteristics? Even though the Government refused a motion to have menopause listed as a protected characteristic in the UK, the protected characteristics of age, gender and even disability have been cited in discrimination cases by women who have lost their jobs when menopause symptoms were actually at the root of the issue.

In the UK, it is reported that only 12% of women tend to seek workplace adjustments to relieve their menopause symptoms, and more than 25% of those who didn't do so, reported that the reason they did not speak up was for fear of the reaction they would get. Silently, they struggle on until it becomes too much and the first the business knows is when they are handing in a long term sicknote or indeed a resignation letter. Too late, and more talent lost. By the way, I have seen it reported that a long-term sickness duration for menopause is reckoned to be around 32 weeks. If that isn't incentive enough for you to step up the conversations and agree reasonable adjustments, I don't know what is!

With regard to those reasonable adjustments, if you think back to what you have learned earlier about common symptoms and then think about your own workplace, you will see straight away that it is so easy to fix issues such as room temperature, adequate ventilation, access to toilets and to fresh drinking water, uniforms that are menopause friendly (temperature and fit), appropriate rest space and lockers to keep spare clothing etc. accessible. There may need to be more thought given to jobs that require concentration for prolonged periods, dealing with stressful situations, perhaps jobs that have limited access to facilities. But this should be done anyway as part of the stress risk assessment against every job, right?

One thing that has changed that is beneficial to women experiencing debilitating symptoms is that more and more organisations since the pandemic have been operating remote or hybrid working arrangements. This could be an excellent opportunity for a menopausal woman to avoid a long and early commute, the ability to control their own environment, ventilation, access to toilet etc and the flexible hours arrangement could be especially helpful if insomnia is an issue and early mornings are something of a challenge.

Organisations and you, if you are a line manager, HR or Health & Safety professional, should have this on your radar and be proactively looking at what you can do to support and retain talent. Many of my client companies have developed menopause policies, I've trained their managers in menopause awareness as well as menopause champions, appointed persons who are an excellent support and signposting authority for women needing help or advice. A reputation as a decent employer who takes wellbeing seriously really can be a deciding factor for people choosing whether to join a business and indeed, whether or not to stay.

Let's just go back to that statistic from earlier though first, where women are not disclosing the truth about their sickness absence, perhaps suggesting it is a tummy bug or migraine or bad back which has kept them away from work. That to me says we need to be working on developing the culture of that business so that women do feel able to be honest, and part of that is indeed the training that I have done with managers to contribute towards that climate.

As well as those crucial conversations at home with partners, husbands, girlfriends and GPs, conversations with managers in the workplace need to be happening too. However, we cannot just expect managers to have the skill, confidence and understanding to do so. If *you* are a manager, perhaps you work for a positive and proactive business, but have they specifically taught you how to have really useful conversations about sensitive issues with your team or have they simply given you a copy of a policy that they have devised and told you to get on with it? Giving you a policy to work to without any skills training to apply it is like handing a novice driver a copy of the Highway Code and expecting them to drive to a high standard – we need skill development opportunities, not just a list of rules.

Do not panic if that is what has happened for you. We are about to explore the issue of workplace conversations about the peri/menopause so panic ye not!

Now, before we begin, let's be really clear, I am absolutely *not* suggesting for one moment that during a team meeting you casually start asking team members about their peri/menopausal status, nor should you suddenly ask "Could it be your hormones Mary?" in the middle of an appraisal review! In fact, can I strongly discourage you from such actions?! Instead let me guide you to conversations with women if there are absence issues, if you are conducting return to work interviews, noticing performance dips, any behaviour changes, where menopause *could* be at the root of it. As I said, there has been an increase in employment tribunals where women have been managed down the poor performance route and been dismissed when menopause symptoms were impacting on her wellbeing and causing the performance issues.

However, just because *you* might want to talk about this, many women believe they just could *not* discuss such a thing with their boss. Why would that be?

Let's imagine for a moment, if you are indeed one of those women who feel they have no support at all from your employer and if the thought of discussing your perimenopause symptoms with your boss sends your anxiety levels racing, how do we approach this?

We need to change the culture to change the outcome and leadership behaviour is a massive contributor to culture shift (but that is for another book, watch this space!). As a leader (if you are one), your attitude, your behaviour, your knowledge, and understanding is a *massive* game changer.

If your organisation is hosting menopause awareness events, get your backside along there and support the initiative. Be publicly seen as a male ally with an emotional intelligence level sufficiently developed that talk of periods and vaginal dryness doesn't send you running for the hills. Actively support initiatives like this by promoting them in your team, let your team know that you appreciate the challenges this transition *can* present for 80% of women. Through your own language and behaviour, let them see that you are comfortable to have conversations that matter and are keen to learn *how* to do that (by attending and supporting events, etc.)

If your organisation is *not* smart enough yet to be hosting such events, be the instigator! Look out for fabulous people like me to come in and help start the ball rolling with a Lunch and Learn session, with a keynote speech on your Wellbeing Day, signpost them to my podcast so that they can start to educate themselves quietly, share a copy of this book why don't you?!

Changing the culture is the place to start if women in your business are uncomfortable, feel support is lacking and feel the need to lie about the reason for their absence. Make it your mission my friend!

Take a moment to think about what you have learned so far and consider the challenges a working woman might face. Imagine for one moment you are not quite firing on all cylinders after another rough night with little sleep? Imagine you got caught out on the way to work with sudden and unexpected heavy flooding, and I don't mean rain, which meant you had to go home to change, arriving late at work, flustered, and embarrassed about the reason? Perhaps you are confused by new software recently introduced or are struggling to retain information in a briefing meeting, but you don't want to look stupid and incompetent in front of your peers, so you bumble along, humiliated and lacking confidence? It might be that your nerves are in tatters and that angry customer has tipped you over the edge and you find yourself in floods of tears, but you are desperately trying to hold on to it as people will judge you and you might even lose your job!

Imagine, eh?

And all because of something that is naturally occurring, happens to every woman, and just needs a little support and possibly a temporary reasonable adjustment to get over. If you struggle to put yourself in their shoes, imagine this is happening to someone you care about – maybe your wife/partner/girlfriend/mum/sister/best mate and *she* is being managed down the poor performance route and on the way to dismissal. How would you feel about that, knowing what you now know?

Whatever their situation, if their symptoms are causing them problems, even having a negative impact on their work or their attendance, surely you can see the benefit in them feeling safe to have a conversation that could improve matters with someone they can trust? Why not make that you?

Now, let's be clear, you don't need to get into sensitive, intimate information that is beyond your scope. You can simply listen and acknowledge that perimenopausal symptoms can have a negative impact *and* explore what they are doing to get the help they need.

Does your business have an EAP (Employee Assistance Programme)?

Would a referral to Occupational Health help?

Do they need time off to go to a GP appointment?

Can you signpost them to your appointed First Aider for Mental Health if they need support with such issues?

Your role is to listen, understand, signpost to appropriate help and work with them to create a plan for action, that is relevant to their work and the workplace, that shows you are supporting *but* that they are in control of. Yes, they may be experiencing challenging symptoms, but we must strike a balance with what is reasonable and appropriate, and the responsibility they personally have for their own wellbeing and ability to attend work. This is *not* all about the business bending over backwards and them using it as a convenient "excuse" – although I have yet to meet a single woman who has done that, but I know the cynics will be out there!

Please don't forget though that the Menopause is covered by certain pieces of legislation in the workplace to protect employees, including both the Equality Act 2010, where the three protected characteristics of age, sex and disability are covered, and the Health & Safety at Work Act which places an obligation for safe working, as I suggested earlier. This extends to safe working conditions when experiencing menopausal symptoms and will also include opportunities for requests for reasonable adjustments during this time. Organisations such as ACAS and Trade Unions have also published guidelines on this topic and so employers have no excuse – the information and appropriate guidance is out there and failing to follow it can leave employers open to grievances and tribunal claims.

What if that topic comes up as part of a return-to-work interview? Brilliant! An excellent opportunity to ask open questions (that are relevant and appropriate to work). Listen to their answers, (listening to understand not simply reply of course), and then agree a plan of action that will work. Also agree a timescale over which you will review that plan.

"Thank you for sharing that information with me, and yes, I am aware that sometimes this transition can cause issues for many women, I am grateful to you for being honest with me.

Help me understand how those symptoms are affecting you at work and then perhaps we can talk about a plan of action to support you whilst you get the help you need. How does that sound?"

You know, the exact same approach you would take with someone who had been diagnosed with any debilitating condition, whether heart health, cancer diagnosis, unusual migraines, diabetes... help me understand so that we can do what we can to help you to get the help you need. You are *not* becoming the help, you are helping them get the help they need as a decent human being and reputable employer.

Right?

Good.

Please do bear in mind that for many women, our self-confidence and self-esteem really can take a hit at this time in our lives, for all sorts of reasons, and this is where I would be encouraging you (if applicable) to be the best boss they ever could have. Make sure you are doing what you reasonably can to minimise the impact of the work or workplace on those symptoms. Give them confidence in you that you are more than capable of having conversations of this nature, that your intention is positive and all the time they are showing you that they are doing what they can to manage symptoms, you will do what you can to support them. Balance has to be there though; they have to be making every effort.

We know that stress can be a real issue for perimenopausal women, we know the effect that cortisol has on our already depleted supply of hormones, and we know that stress can easily become distress and put us on a slippery downward slope if we are not careful. Do think about workplace stress, think about how you can protect women, the help you might need to signpost them to and how your own attitude and behaviour will have a massive impact and make them unlikely to be totally honest with you.

You know now that stress can be an even bigger issue at this stage than it has ever been before as we know that the cortisol/progesterone/oestrogen relationship is an important one. Please do encourage the women in your world to take steps to manage their own stress levels too. Encourage them to put boundaries between work and home, encourage them to leave work at work, encourage them to take the holiday they are due, remind them that they do not need to be available to the business when they are on rest days/annual leave/sick leave. Proactive behaviours to prevent stress are always better than trying to fix a broken brain. Trust me, I know these things. And no, you don't have to be a doctor to know those things!

To be fair, a decent manager will be encouraging self-care regardless of the person and their life stage, and if you want to better understand what effective leadership looks like within the world of work, I've lots of other opportunities for you to expand your knowledge. Take a look at my website for more information.

No employer can afford to *not* be paying attention to employee wellbeing right now – it doesn't mean you become their therapist or counsellor, but what it does mean is that as a leader, you are behaving in a way that is both professional and within the legal frameworks of Health & Safety and Employment Law.

Organisational wellbeing tends to be best achieved when the business, the managers within it and the individual are all playing their parts. Just as you have a responsibility to your team members, they also have a responsibility to themselves and to be doing all they can, so that they can maintain high standards of performance and attendance.

Any old how, I hope that even if you decide you don't need to learn any further, the advice I have offered here will give you a good idea on how to handle workplace relationships with peri/menopausal females. Yes, there is a risk that the law will come and bite you on the bum if you behave in an unfair or discriminatory way, and many organisations have been feeling that bite of late, but how about we focus on being proactive to minimise that risk, and be seen as an employer of choice and a decent boss in today's challenging world? Now there's a thought!

CHAPTER NINE

When Stress Becomes Distress

Trigger warning: talk of suicide.

I have mentioned already the impact that perimenopause can have in extreme situations, and I wanted to talk a little more about this here, from my position as a suicide intervention tutor, qualified to deliver suicide first aid.

I am *not* suggesting for one moment that this is something that happens a lot but I am also not denying that many people have talked about feeling hopeless, worthless, overwhelmed, and unable to cope and so I *do* want to talk directly about that.

We are aware of the increased risk of anxiety and depression at this life stage, purely and simply due to the hormonal imbalance and the necessity of those hormones for our mental health, brain health, mood and resilience. We also know that sometimes women who have never experienced any such issues previously, may experience them as perimenopause gets underway, again simply due to the required hormones starting to decline and the chain reaction impact they have on other functions.

Given that we know this life stage can also find us under pressure with multiple roles and responsibilities, this can also add to the burden we might carry. If we look at statistics for this age group around issues such as divorce, reports to the HSE, deaths by suicide, we start to get a true picture of how stress can easily lead to distress if we are not managing it well. To be fair, for some women, they will be trying everything they can to manage it well, but even then, those damn hormones can get the better of us, so let's have a really useful conversation about those potential moments of crisis.

We know that suicidal thoughts rarely happen as the result of a one-off event or factor but are more likely to happen due to a combination of complex factors such as identity, biology, psychology and life events. We also know that European research done in 2009 suggests that the risk factor for suicidal thoughts at this stage increases by a factor of 7. This risk factor may even be higher where a woman may also have a history of poor mental health, experienced trauma or abuse, been discriminated against, is using drugs or alcohol as a way to cope, or perhaps feeling lonely, isolated, or defeated. Current research will soon throw a better light on that.

By the way, it is also worth mentioning that the impact on the cognitive load can be a huge challenge for anyone with a neurodivergent diagnosis. There is a whole load of research around diagnosis of ADHD for example in perimenopausal women, who until now have not realised they are neurodivergent. The hormone change and the indirect effect of the impact of other symptoms at perimenopause, can bring issues to the fore that they may have just coped with for many years.

For many women with ADHD entering the perimenopause, they can find that their ADHD worsens, again hormone related. New research from ADDitude, an online magazine, showed that 94% of women with ADHD said they experienced more severe ADHD symptoms in perimenopause, stating "For more than half of the women, ADHD symptoms grew so severe...that they called peri/menopause the period in which ADHD had the greatest overall impact on their lives". We know in any case that a neurodivergent diagnosis can be a risk factor in suicide ideation already, and that thoughts of suicide and attempts to end one's life are greater (Glasgow University & ADHD UK research) – so add perimenopause and all it brings into the mix, and you see why I am making specific reference to it here?

We know that oestrogen is an important hormone made by the ovaries, not just for reproduction but for many other bodily functions, including playing a part in the production of dopamine and how dopamine is made available to the brain. It is these differences in the levels of dopamine that may be one of the important factors in the brains of women with ADHD. Remember those chain reactions I talked about earlier, such as the cortisol response? Well, this is another example of such a knock-on effect. The drop in oestrogen may impact the level of dopamine present, explaining why ADHD can worsen for some women during this life transition.

There is no doubt that oestrogen has an active part to play in brain function, and as well as the dopamine impact (which you might know is the "feel good" hormone, responsible for feelings of pleasure, satisfaction and motivation), there are others that are worth noting.

 It is thought that changes in oestrogen levels also impact available levels of:

* serotonin – and this can also have a negative impact on mood
* acetyl choline – which can affect memory and a whole lot more

Without getting too much into a biology or chemistry lecture, it's just worth knowing that oestrogen is a popular little chap. I've already said it affects acetyl choline, but what if I then tell you that acetyl choline has a part to play in our cardiovascular system, where it acts as a vasodilator (check back on those symptoms!), it affects the gastro system, it affects urinary tract and bladder (check out the frequency of UTI's and other waterworks issues) and even more... I've mentioned about memory and learning too, but here is a jaw dropping fact – this little hormone is in abnormally short supply in the brains of people diagnosed with Alzheimer's disease. Quick quiz question – which gender are at greater risk of Alzheimer's disease in later life?! Yep.

So remember at school when we did the "hip bone is connected to the thigh bone and the thigh bone is connected to the..." sorry about that ear worm – but you get my point. None of these hormones are acting in isolation – the chain reaction and knock-on effect is quite startling the more you learn, and challenge at this time in our lives might be external as well as internal, given the busy lives we lead.

Now we start to understand even more why so many women report the cognitive impact of perimenopause as being the more challenging and why mood, along with low mood, depression and even suicidal thoughts can be more common.

In addition to this complete shitstorm of changing hormones changing neurotransmitters in the brain, some of the more common symptoms of the perimenopause (such as brain fog, poor concentration, poor memory, poor sleep etc.) might also overlap with those of ADHD and exacerbate symptoms. Or, as I suggested earlier, for women with ADHD who had been managing to function up until then, menopause symptoms may trigger a tipping point making ADHD symptoms more obvious and a diagnosis then easier to make.

You are starting to get the idea that there is so much going on at this stage in our lives, and so many symptoms that could be one thing or another, that in a way we can almost understand (but not forgive or allow) the frequency of misdiagnosis.

We mentioned earlier about the impact sometimes on our mental health, and we know that women are often being prescribed anti-depressants when HRT or other solutions for perimenopause would be so much more appropriate and helpful. We know that some women end up being diagnosed as having treatment resistant depression, when several attempts to resolve their symptoms are not successful. We also know that certain anti-depressants need a body rich in oestrogen to achieve their full potency, so the whole trial and error can be very tiring and start to make someone feel as though they are fighting a losing battle. If you do a quick internet search you will find some tragic stories of women experiencing perimenopausal symptoms who have taken their own lives, and there are plenty of podcast interviews with bereaved families who suspect that the menopause was at the heart of their loved one's state.

It is also important to point out that so many women feel as though their symptoms are dismissed and their concerns are not attended to. Remember I previously said how so many women did not trust their GP to make an accurate diagnosis and a significant number had to make repeated appointments to get what they needed? The DHSC (Department for Health and Social Care) launched a call for evidence in March 2021 to inform the first-ever government-led Women's Health Strategy for England. This report from nearly 100,000 respondents demonstrated the extent of the issues.

84% of respondents suggested that they (or the woman they had in mind) were not listened to by healthcare professionals and tens of thousands of examples were submitted. Respondents talked about concerns such as their symptoms not being taken seriously or dismissed upon first contact; women had to persistently advocate for themselves to secure a diagnosis, often over multiple visits across months and years (this is across all health concerns by the way, not just menopause!). Even if they did "secure a diagnosis, there were limited opportunities to discuss or ask questions about treatment options and their preferences were often ignored."

I'm not looking to turn this into "the system is unfair to women" and suggest we march against the patriarchy (although it is and I might if I could manage my menopause symptoms <u>and</u> HRT was freely available to enable me to do so!). But we know that time and again, research has shown that women (and girls) have distinct and specific mental health needs and therefore policies, services and practice need to be gender informed. Reports published by the BMA (British Medical Association) make this quite clear, yet in so many areas we don't see the differentiation being made between male and female needs and differences. I mentioned earlier Dr Lisa Mosconi and how her work shows that a woman's brain changes differently to a man's in later life, and how women diagnosed with Alzheimer's are twice as many as men. We really do need to wake up and recognise that men and women have different needs and requirements throughout different life stages – when will we take note of this and fund research accordingly?

climbs off soap box

So, back to my role as a qualified suicide intervention tutor.

If I did *not* draw your attention specifically to these challenging times and to the extreme cases and the increased risks encountered by some women, up against a system where as many as 84% feel unheard, then I would not be doing women justice.

My own experience taught me how much those fluctuating hormones can make a difference. For me, luckily enough, getting the right patch slapped on my thigh (following the private consultation mentioned earlier) stopped me thinking about ending my life and started me looking at how I might enjoy it even more. I've already told you how they will have to pull this patch off my cold, dead leg as I am never giving it up, but according to the most recent research, I never have to. I am simply replacing what my body isn't producing, it's body identical and is doing me no harm – and in fact it may well be that it is improving my quality of life in other ways too. Issues such as osteoporosis, for example, that we associate with "getting old" but actually the Royal Osteoporosis Society reports that "HRT causes your oestrogen levels to increase. This can help to prevent bone loss and reduce your risk of developing osteoporosis and of breaking bones. If you already have osteoporosis or a high risk of breaking bones, HRT can help to strengthen your bones and make fractures less likely." Mind and body have both been reported to have fared much better when hormone levels were replaced.

From my position as a qualified tutor who has worked with literally thousands of people over the years and delivered hundreds of suicide prevention programmes, I do feel it is important for me to address this feeling of overwhelm and help you to help women get the help they need. I know what that overwhelm can feel like. I made plans, I knew what, how, when, where my life would end – and if it wasn't for the daft brown eyes of my brindle hound, this book might never have been written.

Most importantly, I want you to be confident that if a woman (or actually anyone) does show signs or suggest to you that she/they are feeling completely overwhelmed by life, cannot see a way forward, feels as though their situation is hopeless, *please* have the confidence to engage in a meaningful conversation help them get the help they need.

It's important to stress that it is *never* a hopeless situation, it just feels like that right now, and there are solutions and options and choices that can be made; they might just need to look for that help from different people or in different places.

As for our perimenopausal females, there is so much information and evidence out there these days that shows she is *not* losing her mind, she is *not* going mad, and she really is *not* alone in worrying about things in that way.

We need to adopt the skills that we talked about earlier in the book – listening to understand, asking open questions, never judging or criticising or trivialising how she is feeling. Have the courage to ask questions, to invite her to talk openly and then to help her get the help she needs. I know I keep stressing that, but it is such an important factor to get your head around. I am *not* inviting you to step up and *be* the help. I am encouraging you to be the safe space, the non-judgemental listener, the person who is showing empathy, concern for her concerns and reassuring her that she is not alone. Once you understand better how she is feeling and the help that is most appropriate, step into helping her access that.

Never underestimate the power of a single conversation in the fight against suicide.

There is *always* hope, sometimes we just need to look a bit further, a bit wider, a bit harder, but it is there. Always. I'm here as living proof of that and there are fantastic resources available to us including the most amazing Samaritans who are available 24/7, 365 in the UK. These are just some of the people who are trained and can help; who are you aware of at a local level?

Arrange for them to see their GP or Practice Nurse and go with them if they would like that support. (If you find yourself in more urgent, at-risk circumstances, don't wait for a GP appointment, get to A&E.)

Encourage them to be very honest and clear with medical professionals about how they are feeling and let them know that any medication already prescribed is perhaps *not* having the desired effect, or that it is not working at all. Please don't advocate just stopping taking it and writing it off as "doesn't work".

The right level of HRT or combination of medication can take a trial/error process, but some women have reported a very quick improvement once the right combination and dose is found. I know I am one. I was in such a bad state that without my good friend making the decision to drive up from Kent to be with me, things could have worked out very differently. Within a matter of weeks, I was coping much better, sleeping much better, functioning much better and my suicidal ideation passed.

If for any reason your person cannot have HRT, perhaps due to another medical condition or previous issue, please stress your concern to the GP and ask for alternative appropriate support and medication where possible. HRT doesn't fix it for everyone, it doesn't work for everyone as it did for me and many others, and, some women will not be able to access it as easily or have as many choices, so it is very important that you are their cheerleader and (if needed) advocate in such situations.

Encourage them to talk, a lot. To explain how they are feeling. Perhaps that they are having difficult or intrusive thoughts, so be really clear about the challenges they are facing. Please do not settle for just a prescription for anti-depressants that might take a few weeks to kick in and a promise of therapy via the NHS in about 6-9 months. Ask for an urgent referral to the crisis team, talk to someone trained in suicide intervention (GPs are not routinely trained in this area) and explain that whilst they are doing all they can to keep safe, they feel they need extra support at this time. Don't forget the current (2023) PhD research that has been commissioned to investigate whether hormonal imbalance is responsible, rather than a clinical depression and even though more research is still to be done, it is well documented that "There is definitely an interaction between hormones and well-being.

Your endocrine system works in tandem with your nervous system to maintain a sense of homeostasis, or equilibrium. This equilibrium is what the body wants, but when it's not achieved, a lot can go wrong. When something is out of balance with your hormones it influences the whole system, which means you're going to feel it manifest both in your body *and* your mind." (Lisa M. Basile)

I'm not going to pretend that the system is perfect or that the right help will be immediately available, so it is important to create a safety plan, to help them think about ways that they can help themselves to stay safe. Consider any triggers (and how to avoid them) and talk about distractions (and build more in).

Think about accessing other resources such as the Samaritans (dial 116 123) or go to their website for other ways to get in touch (text, email etc.) but contact them and talk to them about what is happening. They will be happy to provide support to both the person who is struggling and members of their family or friends who might be supporting them. They will *not* give you advice or tell you what to do, but what they will do is offer a fantastic emotional support listening service and help you make sense of the thoughts in your mind.

It can also be really helpful to help this person to create a plan to stay safe, and to encourage her to look at the bigger picture and consider all lifestyle choices. Yep, perimenopause can be a bugger for some of us, but we need to make sure we are also doing all we can to support our own resilience AND our overall wellbeing. I work on the theory that my body has got enough to contend with at this stage already, so I need to not make matters worse.

This includes having strong foundations in place such as rest and relaxation, quality sleep, avoiding alcohol, good nutrition, topping up the self-care tank in whatever way works for each one of us. As well as accessing and arranging to put into place other professional help that might be needed, we should also be looking at activities that are going to contribute positively to our wellbeing. Positive psychology techniques, practicing mindfulness, meditation, pilates, yoga, aromatherapy and any other complementary therapy that helps her relax and feel calm.

Self-care does not have to include candles and sandals, lycra and beanbags; it can be absolutely anything that gives that person a sense of relaxation and calm. If it helps to soothe a troubled mind, whether it is a good walk across the fields with the dog every day or a luxurious bubble bath with an aromatherapy bath oil, encourage her to find what works for her.

Taking a more holistic approach, thinking about supporting the mind/body in whatever way is necessary, whether a nourishing diet or talking therapy, cutting back on stimulants such as alcohol and nicotine, practicing breathwork or taking up a new hobby – there has never been a more important reason to look at our wellness. Read up on the subject of gut health and brain health, think about ways in which you can connect with others, prioritise your own needs and wellbeing! Women are notoriously good at putting everyone else first, especially if there are children and families involved, but we have to help them see how much they matter and how they have to put their own oxygen mask on first! Remind them that many other cultures around the world see this transition as a celebration and a time to focus on herself, and encourage her to adopt the same practice.

Find what works and adds comfort, but don't overwhelm or add stress by suggesting a busy 24/7 schedule. Have it in place whilst arranging to get professional help as needed.

What I am recommending is that we respect that every person is unique. Get help from whatever source best suits their personal preference and circumstances. We need human connection as much as we need food, water and fresh air so find it – lots of it, as much of it as possible and encourage them to talk openly about their situation and how they are feeling, with the right support and network around them. It's a great idea if you can also get support yourself during this time – we all need someone to turn to.

Make sure any useful numbers for helplines etc. are easily accessible and can be found quickly if someone needs to make a call urgently. Look at different access methods too as some people will be more comfortable to text than talk, some will prefer face to face and others will prefer the anonymity of the telephone. Explore options and have a written action plan in place.

Try to make sure they have someone around who they know they can turn to at any time. Encourage them to avoid alcohol or drugs or anything that might lower their inhibitions, exaggerate emotions and add further to an already troubled mind.

Find out about support groups in your local area as well as nationally. Take a look at organisations such as Mind, Pausitivity (#knowyourmenopause), The Menopause Charity, British Menopause Society,

Balance-Menopause, look at resources such as the hubofhope.co.uk and online groups on social media, perhaps on Facebook groups like UK HRT and Menopause Support or Let's Talk Menopause & Perimenopause, Menopause Support Group UK and so on.

Above all remember yourself and remind them that what is happening right now is only temporary. It might feel like they are treading water and completely overwhelmed, but help them see this is a temporary situation and encourage them to look at every possible way of giving their body the help it needs, whether nutritionally, medically, emotionally or spiritually.

I want to make a final point about the importance of sleep. We know that insomnia and disturbed sleep are often symptoms of perimenopause and we also know that a lack of sleep will have a negative impact on mood, emotion and energy. Sleep really is the Swiss Army Knife for the human body as it is needed for so many functions. If sleep is an issue for this person, talk to the GP again. Create a regular sleep pattern, look at sleep hygiene, consult a sleep expert (yep they exist and they also told their career coaches that would be their grown-up job – not!). Joking aside, such people exist and a good night's sleep isn't just something they recommend in sitcoms or soap operas, it is an essential component of wellbeing. It's just that sometimes we will need expert help.

Good sleep hygiene may include the bedroom environment being changed, digital devices being ditched, working hours and boundaries negotiated and investment in self-care activities. Whatever works for them, encourage it – but please do not encourage alcohol as a means to sleep. It might make you *think* it helps you to fall asleep, but actually causes so many other problems instead.

Camomile tea, or even a mug of hot milk at bedtime is preferable, cotton nightwear and bed sheets and a dark room with good ventilation. Trying not to get anxious and wound up about getting back to sleep if they do wake up also helps. Otherwise it becomes a vicious circle of anxiety, insomnia and feeling even worse. Look into the use of magnesium supplements but do your research as some forms can cause digestive issues, and we don't need to be adding further to our night time challenges!

Menopause does not have to be hellish. It might be the Second Spring that sometimes feels more like the bleakest winter, but we can get through it, especially with a little help from those around us, and that includes your good self. Well done for staying with me this far!

Chapter Ten

How To Be The Cheerleader

*W*e have explored what perimenopause and menopause are.

We have talked about when, what happens, what impact it can have and how bloody awful it can be for some of us.

We know that everyone's experience will be unique to them, some women may have a bit of a hot sweat for a few weeks, others may find themselves in the depths of despair.

We now understand much more about hormones and the role they play and the impact they have on other hormones and their functions.

We have considered the effect of other lifestyle issues and recognised different solutions will work for different people.

So how can the woman in your life live the life she is meant to live and not retreat into an empty, hollow, lacking in confidence shadow of her former self?

That my friend, is where your cheerleading skills come in! Now that you know what you know, and you care enough to want to make a positive difference, let's take a look at some of the things that might involve.

It is important to say that there is not a one size fits all solution and that different approaches will work for different people and even at different times. We need to be open to exploring and experimenting (safely) and so in this final chapter I am going to suggest a whole host of stuff to simply give you an idea of how different women have dealt comfortably with their own situation.

Again your role as cheerleader and chief encourager might have to step up a level here if the woman in your life really is down on motivation and self-belief. But you can do that, right? You have the skills!

It may well be that she tries something with high expectations but sadly it doesn't deliver the exact outcome she wanted. Disappointment and frustration are not comfortable emotions to carry in a perimenopausal body so sometimes we need someone to encourage us to try something else.

We all need to remember that we only have one life, we need to do all we can to live it, and to enjoy it not simply endure it!

We are living for longer, so let's make sure we are living it in full glorious technicolour rather than riddled with aches and pains and full of misery and sadness.

At the very top of my list, without any doubt whatsoever, is Hormone Replacement Therapy. Yep, HRT. It has had some bad press over the years and I've already mentioned the dreadfully flawed piece of research reported back at the beginning of the century that meant millions of women simply stopped taking HRT overnight.

Plenty of reports out there will tell you the what, how and why of what happened, so please go check them out to understand for yourself exactly what the issue was and why it reached the headlines. Then go take a look at some of the more recent research done by people like Dr Louise Newson, Dr Naomi Potter, Dr Lisa Mosconi and think again about any risk versus benefit.

I am not about to deliver a lecture on HRT but what I do want to say is, the contraceptive pill has more risks attached to it and many women still choose to take it knowing those risks. There are risks in everything we do in life and sometimes we have to sit down and work out the risk vs potential benefit and decide how we want our lives to be.

There is so much evidence to support the difference that is made by simply replacing the hormones a body is no longer producing in the quantity needed. Forget the old tales and scary stories, forget the reference to pregnant mare urine (yes really!), forget the doom and gloom that an older generation might offer and go do some of your own research.

Don't even trust that your GP will have it all sorted and be able to advise wisely on all options. I cannot stress enough how important it is that every woman does her own homework (maybe with your help). Encourage listening to podcasts, reading reports and articles and books, and using the excellent resources I suggest at the back of this book. The key is to really understand what is going on and what she would like to have happen. It is her body, her choice, her life in a post-menopausal body to think about and potentially she has an average of another 32 years of it!

I've said it before and I will say it again, they will have to prise my oestrogen patch off my cold, dead leg as I will *not* be giving it up any time soon. There is no need to. Once my day of menopause has passed and I am post-menopause, my body doesn't suddenly find a hidden cache of hormones that was put away for a rainy day. I have a life to live way beyond that date, so me and my patch and my little dose of yam at bedtime are in this for life! (Surely as my progesterone is body identical and comes from wild yam, that is actually one of my five a day, no? I can count it along with those chocolate beans and those grapes that my wine is made from... OK, maybe not. My bad.)

However, we truly do need to bring an attitude here of being open to exploring, learning and then deciding. We need to realise that decisions we make now may have repercussions or consequences later especially around conditions such as osteoporosis, dementia and cardiac health. Check out the current research and evidence-based recommendations from experts in this field, and encourage carefully researched decisions, not looks of horror and gasps from our mothers who are still perhaps sold on the Daily Fail news story!

There really is now so much more (balanced) research out there with medical evidence that shows the difference that both oestradiol (a form of oestrogen) and progesterone therapy can make, not just for perimenopausal symptoms but for so many other "old age issues". There is research around the impact of hormonal decline on major organs such as heart, lungs, kidneys; research on bone health, reduction in osteoporosis risks, evidence around reducing dementia and other cognitive issues. Heart health, gut health, brain health, and ongoing research at Universities in the UK such as Liverpool and Glasgow.

I cannot stress enough – women need to make an informed decision that is right for their body and their future. Even if they have been told a straight "no" a few months or even years ago, please encourage them to try again. Things are changing all the time, more and more options and varieties are available, and your role here as cheerleader is to encourage and inspire that desire to keep on keeping on finding a solution that works for them.

If they do not want to, cannot take or cannot tolerate HRT for any reason and have explored all varieties and combinations, and worked out the risk versus benefit if they do have any underlying health issue, please know there are still things that can and will help. There are alternative medications, for example, that are not HRT that can help, and a confident conversation with a caring GP should help open up those possibilities. However, let's not forget things that we can be doing to help ourselves too!

Let's start with the importance of really strong foundations and consider one thing that we absolutely can control, whatever our situation or medical history, and that is the fuel we put into our bodies. I am *not* going to use the word diet, as that often conjures up thoughts of reduced calories or hardcore eating plans (neither of which are recommended for women of this certain stage) but instead let's encourage consideration of good nutrition, of which there is a plethora of information out there to enable any woman to make good choices.

We live in a fast-paced, busy world where sometimes our nutrition isn't great. Fast food, processed food, food that is available to us quickly and easily and actually has limited nutritional content. That goes for you too – whether a husband, partner, mate, manager or professional at work. We need to make sure as a minimum that we are consuming sufficient amounts of good quality protein, a rainbow plate of colour with vegetables and fruit and greenery to give us both fibre and essential vitamins and minerals.

It is sensible to cut out sugar which places stress on our system and rather than being helpful can contribute to insomnia, weight gain, blood sugar issues and anxiety. With this in mind, it is also a good idea to reduce the amount of processed food we eat – stuff that turns up in plastic trays and boxes, contains ingredients that we cannot pronounce, let alone describe! We need to be sure we are giving ourselves a good, consistent dose of vitamins and minerals and our food is a good source of them as a start.

Another source of sugar is of course alcohol and you knew I was going to mention this! Not only can alcohol act as a depressant, which is the last thing we need to encourage positive mood, but it is also responsible for weight gain and can make certain perimenopausal symptoms (such as vasomotor issue and sleep issues) even worse. It is important to say that maintaining a healthy diet and a healthy weight is crucially important for us, especially when we start to look at heart health, blood vessels, circulation etc. and alcohol is not helpful in that regard. In fact, alcohol can place stress on our body as it has to work harder to process it and get rid of the toxins. We have enough stress going on in our lives already without adding to it with unnecessary alcohol, sugar and processed food.

Remember what we said earlier about stress during menopause and the impact it can have? Please support changes in diet and nutrition and activity by taking on board some good habits yourself! Don't add to the stress and tension by insisting that your loved one exists on greenery and water as you tuck into another stinky kebab and a bottle of claret...

Also, choosing a nutritionally balanced diet and low/no alcohol lifestyle is another way of helping to combat stress. We can boost our parasympathetic system (responsible for rest, relaxation and rejuvenation) with certain foods too. For example, probiotic food such as blue cheese, yoghurt, kafir, nuts, seeds, berries and even things like cottage cheese are preferable, which also contribute to good gut health, which is important for women during the menopause too.

Gut health is important as many women can suffer from IBS-like symptoms such as bloating, cramps and other bowel issues during menopause. We want to make sure we are topping up the friendly bacteria that will help keep such issues at bay, and we also know that the gut and brain directly influence each other. Studies have shown that a healthy gut can actually improve emotional wellbeing and increase the production of the all-important hormone serotonin, which we know is important for mood and mental health too.

A healthy gut has also been shown to reduce inflammation, increase immunity and gives us a much better chance of overall good health and wellbeing. If you tried to run a car on anything other than the fuel it was designed to use, you know you would not get the best out of it. Our mind and body is exactly the same and deserves the care and attention we should be affording it as this point. I'm telling you all this for your own good too! I know your intention for learning more here was to help the menopausal person in your life, but you'll be doing yourself a favour with this stuff too.

Having a healthy gut can definitely help with energy levels, and foods rich in fibre are important, as are essential vitamins and minerals that we can get from food sources.

During perimenopause we need to think about bone health given that we know how important hormones are in that regard, and how bone density gets worse when oestrogen levels decline, so calcium and Vitamin D are important, as are iron and magnesium in the diet. The last thing you want is to have to give up your cycling or skiing or any other hobby you enjoy together due to a broken hip or other such bone/joint issue.

There is a lot of information available these days on good nutrition not just for physical health but also for mental health and brain health, so please get smarter in looking at ingredients. Both of you can really think about how you can best do yourselves a favour, naturally and easily, without a trip to a health food store where you might spend your whole salary on pots and potions if you are not careful!

However, due to soil quality and food production methods these days, we do need to realise that food alone rarely provides all the nutrients we need so we may need to look at a good quality supplement to top up the tank. It can become very expensive if you don't do your research first, and it's easy to spend a fortune at the local health food store, just because a product has got "meno" in the title! Please judge whether a product is worthy of your hard earned cash by reading reviews and checking the quality of the ingredients, rather than being distracted by a health marketing budget on the manufacturers part! Disappointed, perimenopausal and skint too is not a good combination! Spend your pennies wisely.

There are also certain supplements that can be specifically helpful for dealing with perimenopausal symptoms. Again, do some homework, check the quality and reviews and if you can, know that there are particular experts in this area that you can consult with. I am not one of them, but what I do know from my research is that again, it is worth reading up and taking advice and looking for ways in which you can build resilience and live your very best life!

You might also have realised that exercise, activity or mood appropriate movement is important to all of us especially as we get older. Use it or lose it, right? That doesn't have to be mountain climbing or running marathons! It might be that walk after dinner together that I mentioned earlier or getting out and about with the dog and enjoying fresh air and nature as an excellent way to help boost our system. We know that this helps with our mood, clarity of thought, mental and physical health, and walking with a friend or someone whose company you enjoy has a double whammy benefit of bringing that human connection. Women at this stage will especially benefit from weight or resistance training and lots of qualified practitioners are out there who can help. Even a simple browse on YouTube will bring up some useful exercise ideas and routines that will be helpful and not cause further stress to joints, bones and ligaments.

Other factors to consider if you are going to help women sail through menopause and support their personal wellbeing, is the subject of self-care. Now research tells us that women are still statistically more likely to not prioritise their own self-care over others, especially women with families, older relatives, children, pets and others to care for, work to do, domestic chores to juggle and so on.

However, if we want to truly encourage women to live their best lives *and* be able to help and support others, we need to encourage them to find time and space for self-care – whatever form that takes for them.

A female friend of mine regularly gets up at 5am to go cold water swimming in a local lake – I would no more do that than fly to the moon, so we each have to find our own way and choose what works best for us.

Perhaps rather than dawn open water swimming, their version of relax and rejuvenate is a warm bubble bath with candles and relaxing music? Maybe they will benefit from journaling, baking, gardening? Craft, jigsaws, knitting, dancing to their favourite music in the kitchen wearing just their socks! Maybe they are more inclined to read, listen to classical music, go kayaking, paddle boarding, hiking or hot air ballooning? Whatever works best! Just as each one of us will have a unique perimenopause experience, the solutions that gives us our joie de vivre and capacity for coping better will be unique too! Maybe a spa day, a manicure or simply taking an afternoon nap is their very best self-investment – ask them to work out what works best for them and then please encourage them to do it, consistently and well!

Honestly, if there is one thing that I have learned over the last 10 years is that life is already short enough as it is. We always think there will be tomorrow to do things that matter, we put things off and get carried along by other people's agendas. One day, even tomorrow, it might be too late.

Now I don't want to get all miserable and maudlin, after all, we are talking about engaging in a Second Spring, but I do want to point out that the choices made today *do* affect tomorrow, assuming tomorrow comes. Making choices today to be kinder to ourselves, to MAKE time for things that matter, to truly live our best lives and prioritise our own needs from time to time and as you have persevered with me thus far, I am assuming your relationship, marriage, partnership, job, career, reputation matter enough to you to put the effort in – so do!

Take your own health and wellbeing seriously, both physical and mental health matter, and encourage those you care about to do the same.

"You cannot control the waves, but you can learn to surf" – according to Jon Kabat-Zinn – so in this busy 24/7 world that we find ourselves in, take time to smell the roses and having made the effort to learn more about perimenopause, menopause and post-menopause life, I hope you feel you are in a stronger position to do so? Life throws stuff at us, and during a time when our hormones are fluctuating and our body is changing, we have to accept that it is simply a life transition, and ride the waves in the best way we can.

So whether you are a husband, partner, boyfriend or girlfriend; whether you are a mate or manager; maybe you are a coach and help women focus on goals and achievements, perhaps you are a counsellor and cannot understand why a client is not showing any improvement despite talking therapy and anti-depressants; maybe you are a HR or Health & Safety professional and want to do a bloody good job for the folks in your business, you are now better informed and wiser to the whole life transition that 51% of the population will experience.

Yay for you – and thank you!

And finally...

*O*ver a thirty-year career, hundreds of organisations and industry sectors, thousands of individuals, I have realised just how important the really useful conversations that I have referred to throughout this book absolutely do matter.

The ability to engage in worthwhile conversations where trust and honesty play such important parts, is critical to any relationship we might have. To care about someone enough to give them the time and safe space to talk openly, to listen without judgement or criticism and to step far enough away from our own ego so that we can step into their shoes for a moment and really hear what is being said. All of that takes time and effort and a real desire to make a difference.

Step away from the stereotypical images and the "just kidding jokes" and try to understand what is really going on and how that might make a woman feel. Imagine if this happened to men?

Imagine if you got to a stage in your life where you thought you were losing your mind, you became overly anxious, lost confidence, your willy shrivelled up and became excruciatingly sore and you were so rundown with fatigue and lack of motivation that you just wanted to walk out the door and not come back? Maybe you developed raging acne, grew hair where you didn't want any more hair, your joints ached, your eyes were dry, that "muffin top" around your waistband developed into a three-tier wedding cake and no amount of cranberry juice was shifting that water infection. I reckon there would be a massive investment in the research and solutions, but sadly, for women, there hasn't been.

Thankfully there is a lot more information out there now about this significant life stage, lots more resources, lots more research but I have no doubt that we still have a way to go and more to learn about this chapter of our lives. Please don't let ignorance or ego or pride or shame damage those relationships and, with respect and care, have those conversations.

Conversations can change and save lives. I know.

"Could it be your hormones love?" might be the opening line to the most important conversation you will ever have for your relationship, and said at the right time, in the right place, with compassion and concern, could be just the question that they have been mulling over themselves. Have the courage to ask and the respect to then listen.

Take good care x

Really Useful Resources

*T*here are lots of really useful resources out there these days that can be helpful for you to consider. I have mentioned a few in the main body of the book but thought you might find it useful if I listed some here as an easy point of reference for you. There is also a more comprehensive list on my website www.InHerRightMind.com

I have tried to offer a range of opinions and views, from a number of different sources, so that you can make the best decision for your situation.

My body, my choice.

I have suggested to you my own website as a place to grab a free symptom tracker and other useful resources – https://InHerRightMind.com so please do scoot along there and grab anything useful.

Websites such as:
Balance Menopause

https://www.balance-menopause.com/

Website and phone app – Dr Louise Newson

NHS Guidance on Menopause Symptoms and treatment – https://www.nhs.uk/conditions/menopause/

British Menopause Society and the Women's Health Concern (the patient arm of the BMS)

https://thebms.org.uk/

NICE guidelines on menopause diagnosis and management – https://www.nice.org.uk/guidance/ng23

The Menopause Charity – https://www.themenopausecharity.org/

Health & Her Menopause Experts – https://healthandher.com

Latte Lounge https://www.lattelounge.co.uk/

Henpicked – https://henpicked.net

Menopause Café – https://www.menopausecafe.net/

The Menopause Exchange – https://www.menopause-exchange.co.uk/

Menopause Matters – https://www.menopausematters.co.uk/

Meg's Menopause – https://megsmenopause.com/

Books include:

Everything you need to know about the menopause by Kate Muir

All you need to know in one concise manual by Dr Louise Newson

Menopausing by Davina McCall and Dr Naomi Potter

The Complete Guide to the Menopause – Dr Annice Mukherjee

Cracking the Menopause by Mariella Frostrup

Menopause for Managers by Andrea Newton

Podcasts such as:

Really Useful Conversations

In Her Right Mind

Happy Hormones podcast

The Dr Louise Newson Podcast

The Happy Menopause

The Positive Perimenopausal Podcast

Peri-Menopause Power

The Mid-Point with Gabby Logan

Thriving in Menopause

And many, many more.

Find out what best suits the person in your life and help them to take control of their perimenopause years, armed with all the necessary information and knowing that you have their back.

Let's rock this Second Spring!

Printed in Great Britain
by Amazon

43115857R00096